The Great Tanks

The Great Tanks

Chris Ellis
Peter Chamberlain

Hamlyn
London · New York · Sydney · Toronto

Foreword

Of all modern battlefield weapons, the tank is undoubtedly the most photogenic and best known. Because of the expensive nature of the hardware, its gadgetry and ingenuity, its power, movement and speed, the tank is invested with a glamour which captures popular imagination. It is virtually the symbol of twentieth century warfare. Its story contains elements common to most stories of twentieth century endeavour: imaginative men fighting the 'establishment', eccentrics with vision, ingenious engineers, inter-departmental squabbling, continual periods of alternate financial profligacy and parsimony, major advances in technology, and the interminable committees and reports. And, of course, the wars that caused all the effort and destruction.

Over the sixty years or so of tank development, there have been hundreds of tank designs. Only a few of them have stood out as world beaters or pace setters, and this book sets out to tell the stories behind the most important tanks. The most difficult part of such a project, however, is deciding what is 'great' and what is not. In the starkest terms there have only been three or so key designs which have inspired everything else. 'Mother' and its immediate successors of 1916 introduced the classic rhomboid shape, quite distinct from the crawler tractors and more suitable for cross-country movement under all conditions. The Renault FT 17 introduced the classic basic layout copied by virtually all tank designers ever since. And Christie's M1928 first demonstrated that fast tanks were a practical production proposition, although it was not in fact the first 'fast' tank. Almost everything else produced in the tank field has been a refinement of these ideas. So beyond these classic designs we have selected vehicles which have carried on the basic principles to good effect (such as the T-34) or have proven themselves as classics in other ways (the right design at the right time – like the Sherman – or very superior fighting vehicles, like the Panther or Centurion). Inevitably this has led to one or two omissions, of tanks which might be claimed as 'great'. The final criterion in selection, however, was what the design led to. Thus, though British infantry tanks did not lead to further tank designs – the line just petered out, tactically obsolete – the significant development was the refinement of the special purpose tank, the so-called 'funnies' which the British brought to a fine art in the last years of the Second World War.

C.E. & P.C.

Preceding pages:
Super Shermans of the
Israeli Defence Forces.

Acknowledgments The Publishers are grateful to the following for the illustrations reproduced in this book: Associated Press Ltd; John Batchelor; Bellona Publications; Bundesarchiv, Germany; Camera Press Ltd; Central Office of Information; Central Press Photos Ltd; Fox Photos Ltd; Imperial War Museum, London; Israel Press and Photo Agency; Keystone Press Agency; Novosti Press Agency; Photographers International; Pictorial Press Ltd; Popperfoto Ltd; Profile Publications Ltd; RAC Tank Museum; US Army Signal Corps, National Archives; Warpics; the collections of Peter Chamberlain and Chris Ellis.

Published by the Hamlyn Publishing Group Limited
London · New York · Sydney · Toronto
Astronaut House, Feltham, Middlesex, England

ISBN 0 600 33949 1

Filmset by Keyspools Limited, Golborne, Lancs.
Printed in England by Sir Joseph Causton and Sons
Limited, Eastleigh and London

Contents

Around the Tank

Centurion tanks of the Israeli Defence Forces move towards the front line on the Syrian front during the 'Yom Kippur' War of October 1973.

Some of the terms used in tank construction and operation are discussed here in simple terms.

Armament and Ammunition: While the main armament of light tanks and some command and observation tanks has been of only machine gun calibre, in most tanks the principal gun has been of artillery calibre. The size of the gun is either expressed by the weight of the shot, for example 20 pounder (pdr), or by the size of the bore, for example 105 mm or 10·5 cm. Ammunition could be high explosive (HE), used in indirect fire against 'soft' targets, or armour piercing (AP).

Various modifications of the AP idea have led to such types as APBC (armour piercing ballistic capped). Smoke shells and various kinds of illuminating 'star' shell have also been used.

Sights associated with main armament have included plain 'open' sights in early and small tanks, a periscope sight, and telescopic sights. Since the Second World War infra-red night sight equipment has become almost universal and stereoscopic range finders have been fitted in some tanks. Ammunition is carried in the tank, usually adjacent to the gun position. Main

TYPE	Armour (mm) max	min	Weight (tons)	Length (overall) ft	in	Width (overall) ft	in	Height (overall) ft	in	Engine type	bhp
Tank Mk I	12	6	28	32	6 (with tail)	13	9½ (male)	8	2	Daimler straight six	105
				25	5 (without tail)	14	4½ (female)				
Tank Mk V	16	8	27	26	5	12	10 (male)	8	8	Ricardo straight six	150
						10	6 (female)				
Tank Mk VIII	16	6	38.8	34	2	12	4	10	3	Liberty V-12	338
Renault light tank	16	6	6	16	5 (with tail)	5	7½	7	0	Renault four-cylinder	35
				13	6 (without tail)						
Carden Loyd Mk VI	9	6	1.5	8	1	5	7	4	0	Ford four cylinder	22.5
Christie T3	12.7	3.2	8.6	18	0	7	4	7	6	Liberty V-12	338
T34/76, Model 1941	47	20	-	21	7	9	10	8	0	Type V2 V-12	500
Tiger 1	100	26	50	27	9	12	3	9	4¾	Maybach V-12	700
Panther Ausf A	110	15	44.75	29	1	11	3	9	9	Maybach V-12	690
M3 Light Tank	38	12	11	14	10	7	4	8	3	Continental 7-cyl radial	250
M5 Light Tank	51	12	13.6	14	2¾	7	4	7	6	Cadillac V-8	220
Cromwell IV	63	20	27.5	21	0¾	10	0	8	3	Rolls-Royce Meteor V-12	app 600
Centurion 5	152	76	45	32	3	11	1	9	7¾	Rolls-Royce Meteor V-12	650
M3 Medium Tank	56	12	25	18	6	8	11	10	3	Continental 9-cyl radial	340
M4A3 Medium Tank	58	17	26	20	7	8	9	11	0	Ford GAA V-8	500
Valentine II	65	8	16	17	9	8	7½	7	5½	AEC straight six diesel	131
Churchill III	88	16	39	25	2	10	8	8	2	Bedford 12-cyl	350
M47 Patton	100	22	51	27	11	11	1	10	11	Continental V-12	810
KV-1	77	32	43.5	22	2	10	11	9	7	V-2KC1 V-12	600

armament ammunition is either 'fixed' (the round and cartridge in one piece) or 'separate' (round and cartridge handled separately).

Armour: A tank is built almost wholly of armour plate, usually either homogeneous armour or face-hardened armour. Armour varies greatly in thickness, and angling the various faces gives the protective effect of a thicker equivalent. Homogeneous armour is most common; face-hardened armour was used extensively in earlier tanks. Aluminium armour has been developed since the Second World War.

Bogie: The assembly on which the road wheels are carried. The bogie is usually sprung, or carries a springing arrangement for the wheels.

Chassis: This term loosely covers running gear, lower hull and motive units. Tanks very rarely have automobile-type chassis.

Cupola: A fitting which enables the tank commander to get the best possible view. In early tanks this might have been no more than a raised hatch with vision slits or peep holes. More commonly it consists of a hatch with armoured vision blocks and periscopes. The cupola often rotates independently.

Glacis: Nose or front plate of the hull.

Hull: Term for the 'body' of the tank. Usually carries the suspension components, which are directly attached to it.

Idler: The non-powered wheel at either the front or rear end of the running gear which guides the track. Position is usually adjustable to allow for track tensioning.

Mantlet: An armoured housing which protects the aperture in the turret through which the gun fits. Mantlets can be internal or external.

Sprocket: The driven wheel at either the front or rear end of the running gear which engages the track to impart movement to the vehicle.

Suspension: The system by which the running gear is carried with the intention of giving the best possible ride. Among suspension systems are the Christie (with long coil springs), torsion bar, volute springs, Horstmann (opposed helical springs), and sprung arm.

Track: The moving crawler band which gives the vehicle traction. It distributes the weight of the vehicle and grips the surface over which it moves. It is driven by the sprocket. Tracks could be rubber band, rubber block (individual shoes), steel, or a combination of steel and rubber. The track is articulated by being made in shoe form with the shoes linked by pins. Teeth, or similar devices, are incorporated in the shoes to provide a guide round the idler and road wheels and to grip (or be gripped by) the sprocket.

Transmission: The means by which power is transmitted from the engine to the tracks, providing at the same times a means of directional control. The transmission incorporates the gear box. In most tanks levers operated the gearboxes to control the respective tracks.

Turret: The traversing housing holding the gun, and gun crew.

Vision devices: Peepholes, slots, episcopes, vision blocks, and flaps, all usually protected, enabling crew members to see out of the vehicle under action conditions. The episcope is most simply described as a periscope with a field of vision covering a very wide arc.

Fuel Imp gall	Action Radius miles	Max Speed mph	Crew	Armament main	Armament secondary	Ammunition (rounds) main	Ammunition (rounds) secondary	TYPE
50 93	27.6 45	3.7 4.6	8	2 x 6pdr	3 x Hotchkiss mg (male) 4 x Vickers mg } (female) 2 x Hotchkiss mg }	332	6272 (male) 30080 (female)	Tank Mk I
			8	2 x 6pdr	4 x Hotchkiss mg (male) 6 x Hotchkiss mg (female)	332	6272 (male) 30080 (female)	Tank Mk V
200	50	8.3	12	2 x 6pdr	7 x Browning mg	208	15000	Tank Mk VIII
22	22	4.8	2	1 x 37mm or	1 x Hotchkiss mg	237 or	4800	Renault light tank
10	100	30	2	1 Vickers mg	-	1000	-	Carden Loyd Mk VI
89	150	27.3 (tracks)	3	1 x 37mm	1 x mg	126	3000	Christie T3
135	280	32	4	1 x 76.2mm	2 x mg	77	3000 max.	T34/76, Model 1941
125	73	23	5	1 x 8.8cm	2 x MG34 mg	92	5700	Tiger 1
-	110	34	5	1 x 7.5cm	3 x MG34 mg	79	4500	Panther Ausf A
45	70	36	4	1 x 37mm	3 x mg	103	8270	M3 Light Tank
74	100	36	4	1 x 37mm	3 x mg	123	6250	M5 Light Tank
116	173	38	5	1 x 75mm	2 x Besa mg	64	4950	Cromwell IV
121	68	21.5	4	1 x 20pdr (84mm)	1 x Browning mg	64	4250	Centurion 5
175	120	26	5	1 x 75m	1 x 37mm/2 x mg	46	178 (37mm)/9200 (mg)	M3 Medium Tank
168	100	26	5	1 x 76mm	2 x mg	71	6250	M4A3 Medium Tank
36	90	15	3	1 x 2pdr	1 x Besa mg	60	3150	Valentine II
-	120	15.5	5	1 x 6pdr (57mm)	2 x Besa mg	84	9450	Churchill III
175	100	37	5	1 x 90mm	3 x mg	71	11500	M47 Patton
129	95-140	21	5	1 x 76.2mm	3 x mg	111	3000	KV-1

The British Heavy Tanks

Mk IV tanks arrive at the railhead just prior to the Battle of Cambrai in November 1917, the first tank attack en masse. The fascines (bundles of brushwood) were to fill in craters, and were carried forward on the tank roof and released as required. In the Mk IV the sponsons could be retracted inside the vehicle to reduce width as shown here, rather than be unshipped. The first vehicle is a female with small sponsons for machine guns; the next two are males with large sponsons for 6pdr guns.

The early actions of the First World War in August 1914 were very mobile as the Schlieffen Plan was put into operation and the mighty German armies swung through Flanders in a right hook aimed at Paris. These were the last days of horsed cavalry actions, and galloping horse artillery. The German advance was checked on the Aisne, and by September 1914 the fighting on the Western Front had changed from a moving battle to a stalemate of trench systems opposing each other from the Belgian coast to the Swiss border and dominated by the fire supremacy of the well-sited machine-gun. The trenches were protected by the massive wire entanglements. In these conditions cavalry could not be used and infantry assaults could only be mounted under the covering fire of a huge artillery bombardment, generally with only limited success and heavy losses to the attackers. Constant shelling of the same area of ground, plus long periods of inclement weather, led to a secondary problem, that of getting attacking forces and their equipment across open terrain which often became a sea of mud for weeks at a time. The High Commands on each side had little choice but to accept these conditions of warfare, and in the absence of a better alternative committed larger and larger forces and more and more guns to what soon became a costly war of attrition.

However, one or two imaginative individuals had applied themselves to the problem almost since the start of hostilities, obviously influenced, if only subconsciously, by the earlier ideas of 'landships' popularised in early science fiction novels. One who was to play an important role later was Lieut-Colonel E.D. Swinton, assistant secretary of the Committee of Imperial Defence, who was sent to France as an official war correspondent ('Observer') in September 1914. From previous study, Swinton appreciated more than most that the machine gun was likely to be the major defensive weapon of the war. The Royal Artillery had ordered American Holt agricultural crawler tractors to tow guns and Swinton had the idea that such a vehicle fitted with a suitable armoured body would make an excellent means of storming enemy trenches by carrying infantry or guns across 'no man's land' safe from enemy rifle and machine gun fire. On his return to London Swinton passed his ideas to Lieut-Colonel Maurice (later Lord) Hankey, Secretary of the Committee of Imperial Defence, who in turn passed them on to the General Staff and to Lord Kitchener, Secretary of State for War. Their official view, however, was that such vehicles would be very vulnerable to shell fire. Meanwhile, over Christmas 1914, Hankey drew up a memorandum on the war situation to date which included special mention of the need for some sort of armoured protection for infantry attacks. This memorandum was circulated to the Committee of Imperial Defence; a member of this committee was Mr Winston Churchill, First Lord of the Admiralty.

Churchill, as political head of the Royal Navy, was already aware of efforts being carried out by the Royal Naval Air Service to provide armoured vehicles for its own use. Hankey's memorandum prompted Churchill to submit a memorandum of his own on the subject of the Army's apathy in tackling the problem of storming enemy trenches by the use of suitably protected cross-country vehicles, and among other things Churchill called for a committee 'of

engineer officers and other experts' to be set up by the War Office to study likely ideas. He also warned that the Germans might already be working on similar lines.

As a direct result of this memorandum, Kitchener was persuaded by Asquith to set up a committee to examine Swinton's ideas, and others which were similar. This committee comprised the Directors of Fortifications, of Artillery, and of Transport, all War Office generals. On February 17, 1915, they witnessed cross-country trials of a Holt tractor towing a trailer loaded to simulate the weight of troops, armour, and armament, but the severe weather conditions at the time caused the vehicle to perform poorly – though it should be noted that Swinton's original idea did not envisage the use of a trailer. Unimpressed, the committee reported adversely on the project, raising once

more the previous reason for rejection – vulnerability – and taking the then still prevalent optimistic view that the war would be over within months, before development could be perfected. For the time being War Office interest in 'landships' lapsed; it was left to the Royal Naval Air Service to take the initiative.

The RNAS had become involved in the use and development of armoured vehicles at the very beginning of the war, when they had modified some ordinary touring cars with machine guns and armour plate to protect the landing strips and seaplane bases (at Calais and Dunkirk) which they had set up for their air squadrons in France. These vehicles had a very limited offensive ability, but did serve to prove to the RNAS the value of armour protection. As a result the commander of the RNAS, Captain (later Rear-Admiral Sir Murray) Sueter, had suggested to

Holt tractors inspired most of the early tank pioneers; here they are shown in their original artillery role, hauling 8 in howitzers into position in Death Valley during the Somme offensive of 1916. The men are sheltering from a nearby barrage.

Tank Mk V, the standard British heavy tank of 1918.

Winston Churchill the use of a tracked armoured device for land warfare, utilizing the British-made Diplock Pedrail crawler tracks. Sueter himself got the idea of using Pedrail tracks from Captain Scott's pre-war Polar expeditions where tracked trailers were considered for transport over snow and ice. Meanwhile Flight-Commander T.G.Hetherington, the RNAS armoured car transport officer, had proposed to Seuter the idea of a giant 'land battleship' with three 40-ft diameter wheels arranged tricycle fashion round a platform which mounted three turrets, each with twin 4-in naval guns, the whole contrivance being driven by an 800 hp submarine diesel engine. The 40-ft wheels were considered necessary to enable this monster to cross the widest (9ft) German trench. This vehicle was not unlike a similar type of 'landship' which had featured in one of H.G.Wells' novels.

The Landships Committee

On February 15, 1915, two days before the Army trials of the Holt tractor, Hetherington was able to describe his 'land battleship' idea personally to Churchill, who, greatly impressed by this imaginative scheme, set up a committee – known as the Landships Committee – under the chairmanship of Mr (later Sir) Eustace Tennyson d'Eyncourt, the Director of Naval Construction, to consider its practicability. Formed on February 20, the committee included Hetherington and various co-opted transport experts and engineers. Its first task was to report on the two types of 'landship' suggested, Sueter's tracked vehicle idea or Hetherington's 'big wheeled' vehicle. On March 26, Churchill, on

his own initiative, authorized construction of 12 tracked and 6 'big wheel' landships, the design for the latter having been scaled down considerably by the committee in the intervening month to a more practical size with 15-ft diameter wheels. In the meantime, Lieut Albert Stern, another RNAS armoured car officer, was appointed secretary of the committee and he was to play a prominent part in organizing its future.

The contract for the 'big wheel' machines went to Foster's of Lincoln, whose commercial Foster-Daimler 105 bhp petrol (gasoline) tractors were already being used to haul big guns for the Royal Marines Artillery in France; it was proposed that components from the tractors could form the basis of the 'big wheel' machines. Concurrently work proceeded on the crawler track 'landship' under the supervision of Colonel Crompton, a veteran engineer whose transport experience dated back to the Crimean War. One of his assistants was Lieut W.G.Wilson, another RNAS armoured car officer who had been a notable automotive engineer before the war. The Diplock Pedrail tracked 'landship' design proved impractical when it was realised that the vehicle was too long (over 40ft) to negotiate corners in the narrow lanes of France. Also the Pedrail and its mode of drive was complicated and under-powered. In early May 1915, therefore, work on these vehicles was suspended, the prototype being eventually handed over to the Army for proposed service as a flamethrower vehicle, though it was never subsequently used. An articulated chassis was now deemed necessary to give the required flexibility for manoeuvring and an RNAS officer was sent to the United States to purchase two Bullock Creeping Grip Caterpillar tractors to serve as a basis for the articulated design. While in the USA, the officer was also instructed to order two sets of lengthened Bullock tracks and suspension components, since those on the standard Bullock tractor were a little short for crossing a 5-ft trench or surmounting a 2½-ft parapet – the minimum performance characteristics thought desirable by the committee. The Bullock tractor was an agricultural machine, chosen as being most suitable for the job after the Landships Committee had witnessed a demonstration of its capabilities on Greenhithe Marshes.

In June 1915 the two Bullock tractors arrived in Britain and were taken to a new testing ground which the RNAS had established at Burton-on-Trent, adjacent to the famous brewery. Lieut Wilson was placed in charge of the test programme. Meanwhile construction of a full-size wooden mock-up of the 'big wheel' machine at Foster's showed that even with 15-ft wheels, such a vehicle was too big to be practical, so this

The Daimler-Foster 105 bhp petrol tractor, here seen on military trials, provided the engine used in the first British tanks. Foster of Lincoln, who built the tractor, also built the first tanks.

Two Creeping Grip tractors purchased from America in 1915 were tested as the basis for a proposed articulated 'landship'. The Creeping Grip tracks, suitably lengthened, were used on 'Little Willie'. Far right in this picture is Major W.G.Wilson, designer of the first British tanks, with Major Hetherington.

project was cancelled at the end of May 1915. The articulated version of the 'landship' was also doomed to failure; tests showed that the stresses imposed on the coupling between the two tractors were too great when crossing trenches and, despite its flexibility, the complete articulated vehicle was still too unwieldy.

Work on the articulated 'landship' was abandoned, and the Landships Committee decided instead to build a new experimental 'landship' equivalent to one half of the articulated version. On July 22 therefore, Mr (later Sir) William Tritton, chief executive of Foster's, was asked to undertake this task utilizing the lengthened Bullock tracks which had been brought over from America. The order was confirmed two days later, and Lieut Wilson was seconded to Foster's to help Tritton with the design as a service (and Landships Committee) representative.

Utilizing the Bullock track and suspension units ready to hand, plus a standard 105 bhp Foster-Daimler petrol engine, also readily available, work on the new design, known as the 'Tritton' or 'No 1 Lincoln Machine', was rapid. By August 11 construction had started, the machine having a box-like body of boiler plate while a dummy turret simulated a revolving turret with 2 pdr gun which was planned to be fitted later. Overall height was 10 ft 2 in and the weight was about 14 tons. To aid stability and assist steering a hinged steering 'tail' of two 4½ft wheels on a bogie frame was fitted at the back. On September 10, 1915, the 'No 1 Lincoln Machine' had its first trials and promptly ran into trouble, since its tracks proved inadequate

for a vehicle of its size. The track centres were narrow, the grip was poor, and the tracks had a tendency to shed. Improvements were needed, and Tritton and Wilson took the vehicle in hand accordingly. After much experimentation they produced an entirely new design of track with lengthened track frames, rollers, and shoes of cast steel which were riveted to links which in turn had guides to engage the insides of the track frames. This new – and much simplified – form of track and suspension became standard for all future British tanks produced in the First World War. With new tracks, the vehicle was rebuilt by December 1915 and in its modified form it was named 'Little Willie'. It was, however, already outmoded before completion, such was the pace of events and the flood of fertile ideas.

While the 'No 1 Lincoln Machine' was running its trials the previous September, Wilson had already perfected the brilliant idea which was to evolve into the tanks which eventually reached production. A major drawback of the 'No 1 Lincoln Machine' was its instability, which threatened to overturn it if it tackled a parapet more than 2½ft high. The standard German trench parapet was 4ft high and the 'Big Wheel Machine' had been calculated mathematically to run over parapets of this height. Wilson therefore drew up a new scheme for the vehicle which retained the hull of the 'No 1 Machine' more or less unaltered but carried the tracks around the full height of the hull in such a form that the lower run which contacted the ground was shaped approximately like an arc from a 60-ft diameter wheel. The advantages of

the 'Big Wheel' idea were thus integrated with the compact form of the crawler track 'landship', giving rise to the now-classic lozenge shape associated with the tank.

A wooden mock-up of the idea was shown to the Landships Committee when they witnessed the trials of the 'No 1 Lincoln Machine' in September. The advantages of the new design

Far left The mock-up in wood of the proposed 'big wheel landship', abandoned before completion.

Above 'No. 1 Lincoln Machine', or 'Little Willie', tackles a ditch during trials after modification in December 1915.

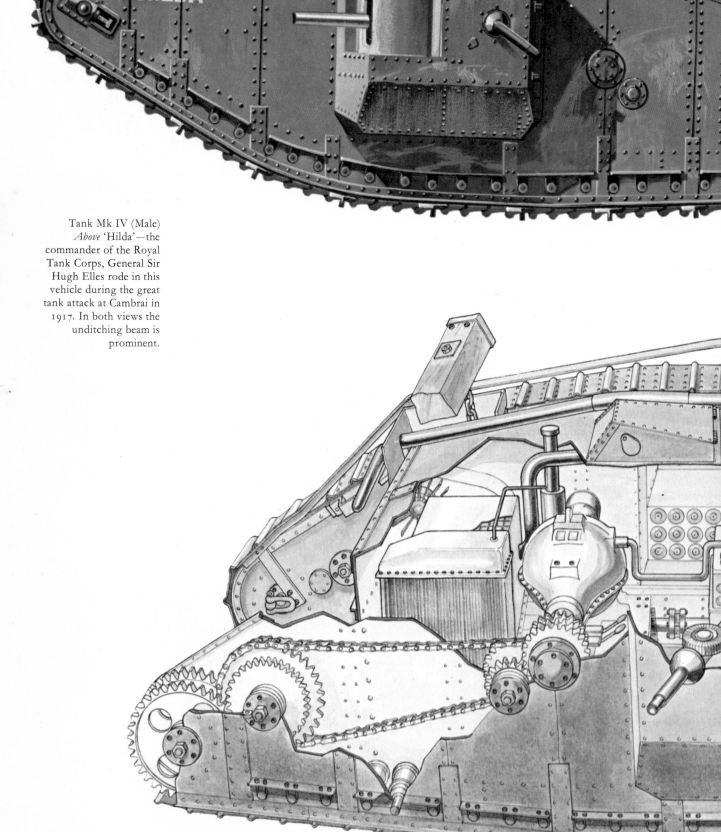

Tank Mk IV (Male)
Above 'Hilda'—the
commander of the Royal
Tank Corps, General Sir
Hugh Elles rode in this
vehicle during the great
tank attack at Cambrai in
1917. In both views the
unditching beam is
prominent.

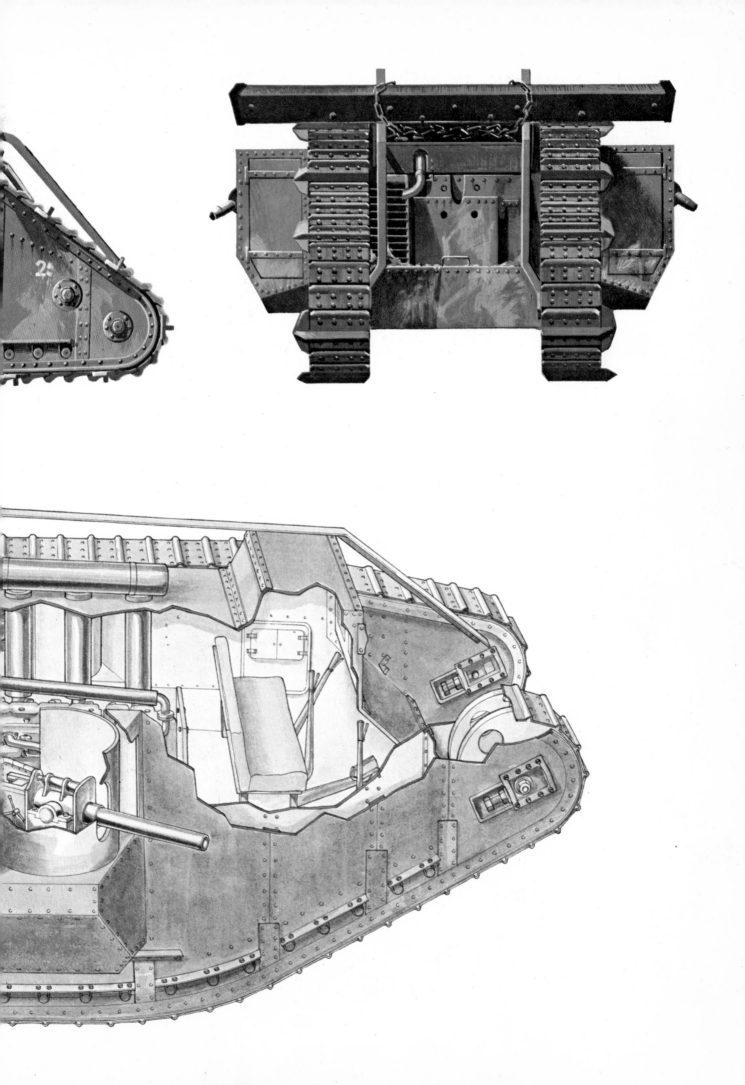

'Mother', prototype for the production British tanks, demonstrating her ditch-crossing ability on her initial trials.

Tanks Mk I in production at the Foster works, 1916.

One of the first Mk I tanks is driven on to a railway flat for delivery from the Foster factory. Sponsons are not yet fitted. The legend on the side says 'With care to Petrograd' in Russian as a deceptive security device.

were obvious, particularly as it met new requirements laid down by the Army, and recently passed to the committee, for an 8 ft trench-crossing ability. To keep down the height and thus reduce the centre of gravity, the modified design dispensed with the turret and the armament was placed in sponsons, one each side of the vehicle.

Revived Army Interest

Meanwhile Colonel Swinton had continued his efforts to get the Army interested in 'landships'. He submitted a paper on the subject to GHQ in France and with the help of an interested staff officer was put in contact with the Landships Committee which Churchill had set up. This staff officer, Major Glyn, was instrumental in persuading the General Staff to liaise with the Landships Committee, as a result of which four War Office representatives were invited to join the committee at the end of June. Swinton's ideas, including his views on armament and trench-crossing ability for future 'landships', could thus, through the committee, now reach the men who were actively working on the 'landships' experiments. Features suggested by Swinton, including 6 pdr rather than 2 pdr guns and 10–12 mm armour thickness, were incorporated in the new lozenge-shaped machine which Wilson and Tritton were building. This vehicle, known variously as the 'Centipede', 'Big Willie' and finally, 'Mother', was first run on December 3, 1915, at Foster's works. At about this time the name 'tank' was first adopted in place of 'landship', for security reasons. To answer the curious workers who could not avoid seeing the new vehicle, it was described as a 'water carrier' which was soon shortened to 'water tank', then to 'tank'.

'Mother' was fully completed by January 26, 1916, and sent secretly to Hatfield Park for a full scale demonstration to the members of the Landships Committee and other interested parties. A tough obstacle course was laid out, simulating British and German type trenches and parapets, craters, ditches, barbed wire entanglements, streams, and so on. 'Mother' took all in her stride, including a 9 ft trench which was a foot wider than the maximum width of crossing asked for. On February 2 the same demonstration was repeated for the benefit of cabinet ministers and senior officers, including Lloyd George, who was then Minister of Munitions, and Lord Kitchener. Though Kitchener remained sceptical, calling 'Mother' a 'pretty mechanical toy', the others present were very impressed. Lloyd George had been kept informed of developments over the previous six months and it had been agreed that the Ministry of Munitions would become responsible for production once a satisfactory prototype tank was ready. The Landships Committee was thus now re-constituted as the Tank Supply Committee with Lieut. Stern as chairman and Swinton as a member.

Events now moved swiftly and on February 12 the first production order for 100 tanks based on the 'Mother' design was placed with Foster of Lincoln (25) and the Metropolitan Carriage and Wagon Co., Wednesbury, Staffordshire, near Birmingham (75). Churchill had not been involved in these latest developments since he had resigned from the government the previous November following the failure of the Dardanelles campaign. He was now a serving officer in France, but had kept abreast of events and at the end of 1915 sent a memorandum on 'Variants of the Offensive', including the subject of 'attack by armour', to the new C-in-C, Haig. Haig's interest was aroused and he appointed a staff officer, Major H. J. Elles, as a liaison officer to the Tank Supply Committee. Elles was later to become commander of the tanks in France.

Production and Organization

It was now necessary to train the men for the tanks, and Colonel (later Major-General Sir Ernest) Swinton was appointed chief of the new arm at the beginning of March 1916. Initially the force was called the 'Armoured Car Section, Motor Machine Gun Service', but in May this was changed to 'Heavy Section, Machine Gun Corps', a more secretive title. In November 1916, after the tanks had seen action, the name was to be changed once again to 'Heavy Branch, Machine Gun Corps', before the name 'Tank Corps' was adopted in July 1917. Meanwhile Swinton toured Army units and officer training units picking a nucleus of volunteers with mechanical experience for training as crews, and the RNAS personnel involved (including Stern and Wilson) were all transferred to the Army with the appropriate ranks. Swinton planned to build up three complete tank battalions each of five companies with 12 tanks each. His plan was vetoed by GHQ in France, however, who wanted a basic company organization, each with 25 tanks. This was the establishment in force at the time of the very first tank action at Flers-Courcelette on September 15, 1916. There were six companies – A B C D E and F – of which C and D arrived in France in August, A in September on the very morning of the attack, and B in October. After the tanks had made their mark, however, and were given their own organization in France, the corps was further re-organized (from January 1917) into battalions each with three companies of 25 tanks each. The existing companies were expanded to form the battalions. By the time of the Battle of Amiens in August 1918, the original six companies had expanded into a great force of 18 battalions, 16 of them in France, with more being formed.

In March 1916 the first training school for tank men was set up at Bisley ranges, Surrey, but three months later, in June, on delivery of the first tanks they moved to Thetford, Norfolk, on the estate of Lord Iveagh. It was from here that the first two companies, C and D, followed shortly by A, left for France in August 1916. By the following November a larger establishment was required to cope with the expansion plan, and Swinton selected Bovington Camp, at Wool in Dorset, as a new 'home' for the tanks since there was plenty of surrounding heathland available for realistic training. Bovington has remained the training base for British armoured forces ever since.

The first 100 production tanks were all planned to be similar to 'Mother' and were armed with 6pdr guns. In April 1916, however, Swinton was instrumental in changing this schedule to include a proportion of vehicles – eventually settled at half-and-half – to have an all-machine-gun armament, the idea being to provide vehicles capable of protecting the 6pdr gun tanks from infantry attack or of chasing fleeing enemy infantry. The tanks with 6pdr guns would then concentrate on tackling enemy guns, fortifications, and defences. The tanks with 6pdr guns were known as 'males' – paradoxically making 'Mother' a male – while the vehicles with machine-guns only were known as 'females'. Approval to increase the initial order to 150 vehicles was obtained at the same time. The 6pdr guns were obtained from the Admiralty, since at the time 'Mother' was designed the Master-General of Ordnance was still unsympathetic to the 'landship' idea and refused to make Army guns available. The female tanks had two Vickers machine guns in place of each 6pdr in a modified sponson. Secondary armament in both male and female Mk I tanks consisted of Hotchkiss machine guns in ball mounts.

Tank Mk I

The Mk I tank was the type used at the Battle of Flers-Courcelette and succeeding tank actions until about May 1917. It was virtually identical to 'Mother' except that it was built of armour instead of boiler plate. Of riveted construction throughout, it was essentially a box with

The first-ever tank attack at Flers-Courcelette on the Somme in September 1916. Infantry are moving on beyond an abandoned damaged vehicle.

lozenge-shaped sides carrying the tracks. There was a raised cupola in the hull front for the driver and for the commander, who was also the brakesman, and a sponson on each side carrying the main armament in limited traverse mounts. The sponsons could be unbolted for transportation by rail to reduce the width and the weight. Sometimes the sponsons were towed behind the vehicle on a trailer on confined routes like country lanes, also to reduce overall width. Removing and replacing the sponsons was an arduous task since each weighed 1 ton 15 cwt and had to be manhandled. There was a round manhole in the roof for observation and egress, but the usual means of getting in or out of the vehicle was through the door fitted in the rear of each sponson.

Other external features peculiar to the Mk I when it first went into action in 1916 were the bomb roof and the 'steering tail'. The former was a tented roof of chicken wire on a wood or wire frame, carried above the hull top to prevent hand grenades from lodging and exploding on the roof. This was cumbersome, fragile, and in practice hardly needed, so the 'bomb roof' idea was soon discarded. The 'steering tail' was the device introduced in the 'No. I Lincoln Machine' to aid stability and steering. It consisted of two iron spoked wheels on an Ackermann steering axle controlled by wires from a steering wheel in the driving position. The entire bogie unit was sprung from the back of the hull which also carried an hydraulic ram allowing the bogie and wheels to be raised clear of the ground for normal travel. A towing hawser and other stores were normally carried on a platform on the bogie frame. The main aim of the 'steering tail' was to give increased effective length for trench crossing and also to assist steering. Very large radius turns or minor course corrections could be effected by the rudder-like action of

the 'tail' with no need to change gear on the vehicle's tracks. While the 'steering tail' was effective on good ground, however, it proved something of a hindrance in combat conditions since it became easily bogged in mud or craters and was vulnerable to shell fire. As a result the 'tails' were completely discarded from November 1916 and steering was carried out by gear changing only. After the Mk Is had the 'tail' removed, most were fitted with a stowage tray on the hull rear between the 'horns' to take the hawser and other stores.

The centrally mounted engine was a Daimler 105 hp petrol type as had been used in the Foster-Daimler tractor. It had a two-speed gearbox with a differential drive to two cross shafts. These were connected inside the horns, to the rear driving sprockets by chain drive and reduction gear. A gravity feed fuel system was used which led to fuel starvation when the tank was reared at certain angles. There was also a fire risk due to the petrol tanks being mounted high inside the hull. There was a tubular water radiator sited behind the engine with a fan driven from the engine. Outlet louvres were cut in the hull rear but air was simply taken in through the normal openings in the hull. The engine exhausts were led straight to holes in the hull roof. To disperse smoke and sparks twin baffle plates were fitted over each hole; some vehicles were later fitted with extemporized silencers and exhaust pipes by the Central Workshops at Erin in France. Steering was effected either by applying the brake on one side, which was tiring for the brakesman (as much effort was required) and bad for the brakes, or by changing gear to neutral on one side and engaging first or second gear on the opposite track. Then the clutch was let in and the vehicle lurched round accordingly. Four men were needed for this operation, two gearsmen at the

differential obeying hand signals from the driver and the brakesman (who was also the commander), who both sat at the front. Once the new direction was achieved, of course, the gears had to be changed again for straight running.

The Mk I, like its immediate successors, was a roomy vehicle, but uncomfortable for the crew. Vision devices were crude, just slits or flaps, ventilation was poor, and the ride was rough since the tracks were not sprung. The armour plate was riveted to un-armoured angle irons and girders (while the armour quality was itself crude), so that there was much 'splash', particularly when joins were hit by small arms fire. Communications were equally crude; each tank normally went into action with two carrier pigeons but other than that, flags (or voice) were the only means of communication. Initially it was planned to pay out a field telephone cable from each tank as it moved forward, but this had obvious limitations and the equipment, although fitted at first, was rarely used.

Mks II and III

Haig's request for a thousand more tanks after Flers-Courcelette was seen by the tank pioneers as a triumphant vindication of their previous efforts. Stern, now a Major, whose committee had been recently re-organized as the Tank Supply Department, instantly placed orders for the necessary armour plate and engines. A man of great energy and foresight, he also realized

Mk II male tank, showing the wide spudded track shoes which were adopted in this improved model. This tank has nonetheless become stuck in the mud.

that the Daimler engine and its associated transmission were the least satisfactory part of the existing Mk I design; at this time, therefore, he took steps to investigate some alternative types of drive and transmission for possible fitting to future vehicles. On October 10, 1916 the Army Council cancelled Haig's order for a thousand vehicles – but Stern was now easily able to reverse this decision by an appeal to Lloyd George. Additionally, while an improved design for the new tanks was being worked out he obtained permission for another 100 of the existing design to be built as an interim type to keep the factories occupied. Designated Mk II and Mk III (50 of each) and produced once again, in both male and female form, these vehicles were similar in all respects to the Mk I save for detail alterations. Most obvious of these were a revised hatch with raised coaming on the hull top and wider track shoes at every sixth link to give improved traction. The Mk III, in addition, had thicker armour, to Mk IV standard. Internally there were several stowage modifications. Produced in early 1917, they supplemented the Mk Is and some remained in first-line use at Cambrai in November 1917, though largely supplanted by Mk IVs by then. They were used in all the earlier tank actions of 1917 at Arras, Messines and Ypres.

Once replaced in first-line service by later Marks, Mks I–III were used either for training or for 'special purpose' roles. Foremost were the conversions to Supply Tanks, in which the guns were removed and the embrasures plated in so that stores could be carried. These vehicles could supplement what they could carry by towing so-called 'tank sledges' which were made by the Tank Corps Central Workshops in France. Each sledge held 10 tons of stores and up to three could be hauled by one tank. The other rôle of the redundant Mk Is was as wireless tanks, unarmed but with an 'office' built into one sponson and wireless equipment in the other. They had a pole mast and spreaders for the aerial. Wireless tanks were used at Cambrai to send back messages, the first time wireless was used in action from tanks.

Mk IV

By February 1917, production was ready to start on the new design to fulfil the main order. Designated Mk IV, this vehicle retained the engine and transmission of the earlier marks but incorporated many other refinements in the light of battle experience. Chief among these were an externally mounted fuel tank with Autovac pump fitted between the rear horns, smaller sponsons for both male and female versions which could be swung inboard rather than unshipped for transportation, silencer and exhaust pipe for the engine, improved internal stowage, short calibre 6pdr guns in the male to improve manoeuvrability, and Lewis guns (later replaced once again by the Hotchkiss). There was also an 'unditching' beam and associated carrying rails on the hull top. Armour thickness was increased to 12mm on this vehicle since the Germans had by this time developed an anti-tank rifle and bullet which could penetrate the thinner sides of the Mk I. The first production

Above An exercise picture which, nevertheless, demonstrates a typical attack with tanks and infantry in 1918. The vehicle is a Mk IV female and has an unditching beam carried on rails.

Left A captured British Mk IV female rearmed by the Germans with Maxim machine guns and in German service in 1918.

Mk IVs were delivered in April 1917, and 1015 were built in the ratio of two male to three female.

The Tank Mk IV was in service in time to take a key part in the crucial Battle of Cambrai, in 1917, the first great tank action where tanks were used *en masse*.

The Mk IV was numerically the most important tank of the First World War. By the fortunes of war it also became the most important German tank. Mk IVs captured at Cambrai and earlier actions were re-fitted by the Germans at their tank base at Charleroi, re-armed as necessary, and used to equip four new tank companies in December 1917, to supplement the existing three with the Germans' own hastily contrived tank, the A7V. In order to distinguish British tanks from similar types captured by the Germans, GHQ, in June 1918, ordered the painting of prominent red and white recognition stripes on the horns and cupolas of all British vehicles. In German service the Mk IV was known as the Beute Panzerwagen IV ('captured armoured vehicle').

Mk V

On March 3, 1917, several Mk I and Mk IV tanks were tested by the Tank Supply Department fitted with the experimental transmissions and power units which Stern had ordered from

much gear changing to maintain a straight course. Last of all there was a vehicle fitted with an epicyclic gearbox designed by Major Wilson, who had been involved with the design of the earlier vehicles. Epicyclic gearing and brakes replaced the change-speed gearing in the rear horns as fitted in earlier Marks and there was a four-speed gearbox on the planetary principle replacing the two-speed box and worm gear previously used. Though the petrol-electrics in particular offered attractive features, they were complicated to produce and it was therefore decided to standardize on Wilson's epicyclic gearbox for future vehicles. This was a most important step forward for it allowed gear changing to be done by one man – the driver – with consequent improvement in vehicle control and handling.

Major Wilson now designed an improved vehicle to feature his transmission. Designated Tank Mk V, it had hull and armament similar to the Mk IV but now also featured a new purpose-built Ricardo tank engine of 150hp which Stern had ordered early in 1917 when the transmissions were being tested. The Mk V went into production at Metropolitan Carriage and Wagon works, Birmingham, in December 1917 and first deliveries were made to the Tank Corps in France in May 1918. Aside from the more powerful engine – which had built-in radiator with intake and outlet louvres in the hull sides – the Mk V had a raised cupola at the rear for the commander, which gave infinitely better visibility from the interior, and which also had flaps giving access to the unditching beam and rails from inside the vehicle. There was a semaphore arm for signalling which could be erected aft of the cupola from inside the tank and an additional machine gun in the rear of the hull. Later production vehicles had wider tracks. By the time of the Armistice in November 1918, 400 Mk Vs had been built, half male and half female. The Mk V began to replace the Mk IV in mid-1918 though many Mk IVs still remained in first-line service at the time of the Armistice. A number of Mk IV and Mk V tanks were handed over to the American Tank Corps in 1918 and became the first heavy tanks to see service in American hands.

Mk V Developments

Though the lozenge-shaped tanks could cross 8–10ft trenches, by late 1917 there was a demand for increased trench-crossing ability. Tritton of Foster's offered the solution of the 'Tadpole Tail' – longer rear horns to replace the existing horns. These were to be built as a 'kit' and sent to France for fitting to existing tanks. The 'tail' increased vehicle length by about 9ft and was quite effective, but trials showed that it lacked

Top Mk V tanks moving forward with infantry at Grevillers in 1918. *Centre* Tanks going forward to cross the Hindenburg Line. *Above* A Mk V tank of the United States 301st Heavy Tank Battn flies the Stars and Stripes during an attack at Souplet in October 1918. The semaphore signal arm is adjacent to the flagstaff.

companies and engineers working in this field. One vehicle had Westinghouse petrol-electric drive which could be controlled by one man and had a motor and generator to each track giving infinitely variable speed control. A similar vehicle had Daimler petrol-electric drive, while a third was fitted with Williams-Janney hydraulic pumps and motors which gave a form of control similar to the petrol-electric vehicles using a pump for steering and speed regulation. A fourth vehicle was a very complicated type with Wilkins multiple clutches which involved rigidity, especially over rough ground. Thus the idea was not adopted for service. In the summer of 1918 tests were carried out with 6in Newton and Stokes mortars mounted on a platform between the rear horns on a 'Tadpole Tail' vehicle. The idea was to put down covering fire ahead of a moving formation of tanks. Other tests were made with mortars in the sponsons. Neither of these ideas was put into practice.

A superior solution to the 'Tadpole Tail' was evolved by the Tank Corps Central Workshop. An extra 6ft of side panelling was simply inserted into a vehicle which had been cut in two. This gave longer ground contact with no loss of rigidity and had the added advantage of giving greatly increased internal capacity, ideal for carrying stores or infantry. Up to 25 infantrymen could be accommodated and the idea of using these vehicles to carry troops was tried at the Battle of Amiens in August 1918. However, due to the poor ventilation in the tank the troops were in no condition to fight when disembarked. As modified the vehicle was designated Mk V* and was used mostly as a store carrier in the closing months of the war. Of 579 vehicles converted (additional to vehicles used unconverted as Mk Vs), 327 were in service by the time of the Armistice and another 23 were used by the United States 301st Tank Battalion, together with 12 standard Mk Vs. This unit was the sole US tank battalion with British tanks and operated under British control.

A refinement of the Mk V* was the Mk V** which was mechanically and physically similar except that it was built (by Foster's) as a lengthened vehicle from the start. The commander's cupola in the V** was brought forward immediately behind the driver's cupola. Only 25 Mk V** tanks were built and none were completed until after the war. Most were used in post-war days as the British Army's first bridge-laying and mine-clearing tanks in an experimental R.E. squadron. Initial orders for the Mk V** had totalled 200 vehicles, but this was reduced just before the Armistice in anticipation of the Mk VIII which was scheduled to go into production soon.

Fittingly the Mk Vs were in at the kill. On August 8, 1918, nine battalions of them (324 vehicles in all) spearheaded the great opening phase of the Battle of Amiens – the turning-point of the First World War. In September they led the way across the Hindenburg Line, and by the first week in November four British tank battalions were poised ready to push through the Forest of Mormal towards Mons. They never completed this operation because the Armistice of November 11 brought four years of bitter fighting to a sudden end.

It is interesting to note that neither the French nor the Germans produced *successful* heavy tanks during the First World War. Both nations suffered from the error of not thinking beyond the original requirements. The Germans with their monstrous A7V tank and the French with their St. Chamond and Schneider types both simply followed up the first obvious idea of putting armour over the chassis of a Holt

Top Infantry were first carried into action in tanks at the Battle of Amiens in 1918. The Mk V* gave extra interior space. *Centre* 'Tadpole Tail' was an unsuccessful attempt to gain extra track length. *Above* Mk V** was a lengthened Mk V.

tractor – exactly like Swinton's original idea. This led to cumbersome top-heavy vehicles which lacked traction and grip, were unstable and vulnerable. They would 'belly' and be stranded like a whale across a trench. By the time the successful nature of the British rhomboidal tanks had been recognized both Germany and France built designs of their own with 'all round' tracks – the German A7V/U of this type was a close copy of a British Mk V – but the war ended before they could see service.

Mk VIII

The finest of the British tanks of the First World War was the Mk VIII, variously known as the 'Liberty' or 'International', which for a short period (curtailed by the 1918 Armistice) was adopted as a 'standard' heavy tank for the Allied nations.

The Mk VIII design was the natural culmination of the whole series of British rhomboidal tanks. In 1916 control of tanks had passed fully to the Army under the Ministry of Munitions, whose Mechanical Warfare Supply Department was established at 17 Cockspur Street, London. This section was responsible for the designs of all the later British tanks of the First World War, although, aside from the Mk VIII and Mk IX, almost all the MWSD designs existed only in experimental or projected forms.

Design work on Mk VIII actually began in the summer of 1917, and from the start a determined effort was made to ensure success. It was decided that all the lessons learned from previous tank experience would be incorporated into the new design. To give him an 'on the spot' appreciation of the problems then being encountered in tank warfare on the Western Front, the chief draughtsman was sent to the Ypres battlefield to see how existing tanks behaved and handled over the muddy, shell-pocked terrain.

That same September, US Army head-quarters in France decided to establish a Tank Corps, with a field strength of five heavy and 20 light battalions, together with headquarters, depots and workshops in France and a training centre in America, with two further heavy battalions and five light battalions. Major James A. Drain was the staff officer responsible to General Pershing (commanding the US Expeditionary Force) for most of the initial planning, and a provisional order was placed for 600 British Mk VI tanks to equip the new arm. At this time the Mk VI existed only as a mock-up and the Mk VIII was already in the design stage in Britain. When Stern came on the scene as Allied Commissioner, events moved fast. The Mk VI tank order was cancelled the following December and the Mk VIII became the basis of America's tank programme.

American involvement in the Mk VIII project started at an early date, immediately after America's declaration of war against Germany in April 1917. This led to a US Navy delegation witnessing a tank demonstration at the MWSD experimental ground at Dollis Hill in June 1917 to assess the suitability of the new arm for the US Marine Corps.

The US Military Attaché in London, however, considered that the tank was more properly an Army weapon and arranged for a US Army technical specialist to join the Mk VIII programme. The officer sent was Major H. W. Alden who in peacetime was a well-known industrial expert. He arrived in London on October 3, 1917, and subsequently played an important role in modifying the original design to fit it for mass production.

The International Plan

Lt. Col. Albert Stern, originally secretary of the RNAS Landships Committee back in 1915–16, had meanwhile been made Commissioner of Mechanical Warfare, charged with co-ordinating tank production between the Allied nations. Stern established an office in Paris where he contacted both Major Drain, General Pershing's representative, and M. Loucheur, French Minister of Munitions. With Alden included in the consultations, Stern was able to draw up a mutually agreeable brief on future plans and requirements, and the order of priorities. Salient features of this, as submitted to Churchill, then Munitions Minister, on November 11, 1917, were:

1 That a partnership of the USA and Great Britain should be incorporated at the earliest possible date for the production of 1500 heavy tanks to be erected in France.

2 A number of these tanks should be supplied to France if she should require them in order to further the higher purpose of Allied unity.

The A7V/U was the German attempt to copy the British 'rhomboid' shape but was not in production before the Armistice ended development.

Mk V* crossing the Hindenburg Line in 1918 with an infantry mortar team in company. Note the heavy wood crib ready for dropping into a crater or ditch.

A Mk IV female with an unditching beam at Peronne during the German offensive of March 1918.

3 It might be convenient for France to supply an erecting shop without depleting her other resources, but it might be wiser in any case to build a new erecting shop.

4 No insuperable difficulties could be seen for joint supply of components: 6pdr guns, ammunition and armour by Britain: engines, transmissions, forgings, chains and other components by the USA.

5 The design should be founded on British experience with USA ideas and resources. It would eliminate most of the faults of the earlier heavy tanks in horsepower, loading, and trench crossing.

6 Major Alden would collaborate in making the working drawings of the new design before Christmas in London: all facilities of English engineers, draughtsmen, and drawing offices

would be put at his disposal. The design should be agreed upon by the USA and Great Britain.

7 Labour other than skilled might be met by imported Chinese.[1] The French authorities saw no local difficulties in accommodating such labour.

8 It was hoped to work up to 300 tanks a month after April 1918.

9 A very high specified priority should be given by the three governments concerned in raw materials, labour, factories and transport.

10 The entire management should be in the hands of the British and American Commissioners jointly with the French Commissioner where it concerned France.

This document made the first reference to the 'Liberty' appellation often given to the Mk VIII by virtue of its power plant. A note with the brief gave the following comparison between the contemporary Mk IV and the projected Mk VIII:

	Mk IV	Mk VIII (Liberty type)
Power:	100bhp	300bhp
Crossing power: (i.e. trenches)	11ft	14ft
Weight:	28 tons	38·8 tons

France subsequently played little part in the scheme, due to lack of resources in men, material, and plant, but this brief formed the basis of the important Anglo-American Tank Agreement which followed. Churchill approved the scheme early in December and Stern was then appointed British Commissioner and Major Drain as American Commissioner, their task being to draw up and implement a Treaty. The first Anglo-American design conference on the Mk VIII took place at GHQ, France, on December 4.

Work on design was made the responsibility of a committee headed by Stern and Drain, and including Major Alden, Sir Eustace d'Eyncourt of the Mechanical Warfare Dept. and Major Green of the Tank Corps. Next the Commissioners were able to persuade Lloyd George, the Prime Minister, that the Treaty be made at the highest level and on January 19, 1918 it was formally signed by Mr Walter H. Page, US Ambassador in London, and Mr Arthur Balfour, Foreign Secretary. It agreed on the building of a factory in France to produce 300 tanks per month and capable of expansion to at least 1200 tanks per month. Almost incredibly it called for the production of

the first 1500 by the end of the year. The components were to be manufactured and shipped to France as follows:

United States: engines complete with starter and clutch; radiator, fan and piping; silencer; electric lighting; dynamo and battery; propeller shaft and complete transmission, including main gearbox; brakes; roller sprockets; gear shift and brake control; track links and pins; rear track sprockets, hub and shafts, front idler hub and shafts, track roller, track spindles, and bushings.

Great Britain: bullet and bomb-proof plates; structural members; track shoes and rollers; guns, machine-guns, and mountings; ammunition racks and ammunition.

The price agreed per tank was £5000, subject to adjustment.

The scene was thus set for the most ambitious tank building programme yet envisaged. Here was the supreme war machine, the most refined tank yet built, which would spearhead the armoured onslaught on Germany in 1918 and 1919. A triumph of Allied co-operation, the Mk VIII would be the world's first truly mass-produced tank, representing a marriage of American industrial skill with British inventiveness and experience. In fact, none of these high ideals ever materialized. Instead, the Anglo-American tank was defeated by time, attrition and inexperience, which combined to render the whole grandiose scheme almost completely impotent.

The Factory in France

The Anglo-American Commission proceeded in their task with great enthusiasm, establishing an office and design centre in London. The factory was built at Neuvy-Pailloux, about 200 miles south of Paris. This had enough land adjacent for a test track and training ground. Siting of the factory was important, because plant and construction materials had to be brought across from Britain, and all components for the tanks from Britain or America through St Nazaire and Bordeaux. But even had a factory been immediately available the scheme was up against a severe time factor if the target of 1500 tanks was to be achieved by the end of 1918. To build such a factory from scratch on foreign soil in time of war was a fantastic undertaking and progress was slow. In August 1918 the first British firm engaged to do the building was replaced by another, and work was not completed until November, by which time the Armistice ended the War.

The French cancelled their interest in the scheme within only a week of the Armistice, requesting merely 'two or three' vehicles for test and experimental purposes. But even if the

26

[1] The vast UK Tank Corps Dept at Erin in northern France was already largely manned by Chinese labour.

One of the American-built
Mk VIII tanks in US Army
service in 1920.

factory had been ready sooner, it would certainly not have been producing Mk VIII tanks
at anything like the desired rate. Production on
the scale envisaged – or indeed any sort of
production scale – was dependent on the production of the components. British industry in
particular was strained almost to the limit in
1918. The big German offensive of March 1918
proved an added setback due to the need for
replacement material.

An equally serious factor was the failure of
the American aviation programme, which prevented the diversion of the Liberty engines
chosen to power the vehicle. And, finally,
American industry was not well enough organized to produce these engines in anything like
the numbers needed. Despite this, the US Army
had already decided to build a further 1500
vehicles on their own account in America, in
addition to the Allied production programme
in France. However, difficulties with producing
armour plate and guns in America led to a
decision to carry out this production in France
under the same terms as the inter-Allied
vehicles. Britain, in addition, was planning to
build 1450 Mk VIII tanks at home, using British
Ricardo engines in place of the Liberty engines.

Had the war lasted another year, and had the
production capacity been able to match the
planned scale, more Mk VIIIs would have been
produced in 1919 than the total of all other
tanks produced by the Allies in the entire war.
However, by the Armistice, only 100 complete
sets of parts had been completed in Britain, and
then production ceased. The US War Department purchased these components and sent
them to the Rock Island Arsenal, Illinois, where
they were incorporated in a production run of
100 vehicles for the US Army which was
completed in 1919–20. Of the intended British

home production programme only seven
vehicles were completed by the North British
Locomotive Co., Glasgow, when the War
ended. The first of these, a mild steel prototype,
was powered by a Rolls-Royce engine, but the
remainder, built in armour plate, had the
planned power plant of two 150bhp Ricardo
6-cylinder engines arranged as one 12-cylinder
V-type unit. The same main armament – 6pdr
naval guns – was fitted to both British and
American vehicles. But whereas the US-built
vehicles were fitted with Browning machine
guns, the British had Hotchkiss.

The Mk VIII pilot model went through all
its trials and running in America. The mild steel
hull, completed in July 1918, was shipped to the
US for installation of the American-made components. Two officers from the Anglo-American Commission went over to supervise its
completion. As the parts to be produced in the
United States were not yet ready, the necessary
engine and transmission parts were custom-
built for the vehicle by the Locomobile Automobile Co. in Bridgeport, Connecticut. The
completed vehicle first ran on September 29,
1918, and testing began on October 31. At first
no armament was carried, but the vehicle subsequently had two 6pdr guns and ten Hotchkiss
machine guns fitted. This was the only Mk VIII
in the USA with Hotchkiss guns.

The trials were very successful and the US
War Department reported back to Stern in
Paris, at the end of November, that there were
'no structural defects. Machine makes 6mph in
high gear, has ample power for climbing. Has
negotiated 13ft trenches with its parapet re-
peatedly. . . . No engine trouble experiences in
actual tank tests.' Observation on necessary
modifications included the need for 'leverage of
track brakepedal . . . to be doubled to produce

The prototype Mk VIII tank on trials in America. Bringing down a tree made a dramatic official photograph.

satisfactory steering...reduction of width of reverse clutch slots and placing mufflers on top'.

Anatomy of the Mk VIII

The Mk VIII tank bore a strong family resemblance to its predecessors, Mks I to VII. But it was much larger and heavier, with its more powerful engine resulting in a superior power/weight ratio. The track plates were of armour plate, $13\frac{1}{4}$ in deep as compared to the $8\frac{1}{2}$ in of earlier models. The links were strengthened in an attempt to eliminate breakages which had been a persistent problem in the earlier marks of tanks. This was achieved by casting recesses into each link to form stiffening webs. The rear sprocket was considerably enlarged and had roller teeth, this being necessitated partly by the larger track plates and partly to prevent digging in when the vehicle reversed on soft ground. As in previous models, no form of springing was provided, nor were there any track guides; the weight of the track and properly maintained tension were considered adequate. There was no unditching beam or its associated rails as the superior power/weight ratio and extra length

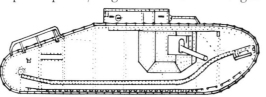

Mk VIII 57mm

was considered likely to obviate the chances of bogging down in mud. Though the track was sturdy, it suffered from a tendency to twist, due to its great width relative to the pitch of its links.

A major innovation in the design was the location of the engine at the rear of the vehicle in a separate compartment; all previous heavy tanks had the engine amidships where the crew were exposed to fumes, fire and fuel hazards. The new arrangement meant that engine cooling and ventilation was physically separated from the crew members, thus contributing greatly to personnel comfort and making for superior fighting efficiency. Cooling of the engine compartment was achieved by inducing air through a forward grille in the roof, allowing it to circulate around the compartment, before it was forced out through a rear grille, over the radiator sited adjacent to the aperture. The Liberty engine was, in fact, an aero engine with a lowered compression ratio and modified by having iron cylinders instead of steel. It was arranged as a V-12 with an independent camshaft for each set of six cylinders and overhead valves. Also fitted in the engine compartment were a water pump for the cooling system, a Ball carburettor, and Delco ignition system. Fuel was carried in three armoured tanks at the rear of the hull, the total capacity being 200 gallons. A fuel pump fed petrol to a gravity tank above the engine and any surplus was returned to the main tanks via an overflow pipe.

Transmission from the engine was by means of a clutch which connected the drive with the reduction gearing. An epicyclic or planetary gearbox contained the reduction gear. Chains transmitted the drive from the reduction gearing to the roller sprocket which in turn drove the track sprocket. There were two speeds which could be used in either forward or reverse, and the epicyclic gears provided for steering by the tracks, a big advance over the sliding speed gearbox with which previous tanks had been fitted.

Engine, clutch, steering and gears were all controlled by the driver who sat in the front of the hull with his seat beneath the central raised superstructure roof. Vision slots in the superstructure allowed the driver to see forward and sideways, and the slots could be closed under fire by rotating protective shields. For road travel, the hinged door in the superstructure front could be raised to give an unobstructed view ahead. The commander stood behind the driver in the central raised 'turret', a fixed box-like structure. He had a small cupola on the centre-line with a vision slit in sides, rear, and front, giving an all round view, from which targets were selected and passed to the gunners. Following the style of all previous operational British tanks, the Mk VIII had side mounted sponsons carrying the main 6pdr armament. These were arranged to swing inboard for transportation. The remaining armament consisted of machine guns only, which were arranged in ball mounts, five in the turret and one in each side door. One of the turret machine guns was in the rear face to fire directly aft. All were demountable. Access to the fighting compartment was via the side doors, and there were sliding doors in the engine room bulkhead, giving access to the engine room from within the vehicle. The hull sides were of an elongated lozenge shape, the rear horns containing the chain drive housing and track adjusting wheel.

In addition to the driver and commander, the crew consisted of a gunner and loader for each 6pdr, a gunner for each machine gun, and an engineer-mechanic who actually sat in the engine compartment when the vehicle was on the move. There was electric fan ventilation in the crew compartment, and an inter-phone for internal communication and target direction. On the original design, and in both British and US built vehicles, there was a machine gun ball mount in the turret sides, but this was subsequently removed on US vehicles and armour plate covered the openings. A semaphore post for signalling was originally to be mounted at the rear but this does not appear ever to have been fitted to production vehicles.

A projected development of the Mk VIII was the Mk VIII* which reached the design stage but, of course, was never built. This would have been 44ft long, weighed 42 long tons, and been capable of crossing an 18ft trench.

Plan 1919

Although the Mk VIII was probably the finest AFV design of the war years, it was never to fire its guns in anger. For the final 'coup' in the west, Colonel (later Major-General) J.F.C. Fuller had formulated the 'Plan 1919' – an historic staff document for its influence on the formulation of armour tactics between the wars. The Mk VIII was the key weapon. These tanks would initiate a breakthrough, following the tactics which had proved so successful at Cambrai. But this time the heavy tanks would roll forward in hundreds, punching huge gaps in the enemy front line for the medium tanks to follow and race through to disrupt the enemy's rear areas and communications. 'Plan 1919' even envisaged the use of air supply of ammunition and fuel to keep the tanks moving in the great breakthrough, with supply tanks to accompany the fighting tanks. Another 20 years were to pass before tactics of this nature were actually ever employed in war – and the Germans were the initiators then with their 'blitzkriegs' in Poland and Flanders.

The 100 American Mk VIIIs, mainly equipping 67th Infantry (Tank) Regt., were used only on exercises and training in peacetime in the USA, where they were employed in the more traditional infantry support role.

With the appearance of the new American tanks in 1932, the Mk VIII was withdrawn from service and most were dumped in the tank 'graveyard' at Aberdeen, Maryland, where they rusted away until 1939. However, during the Second World War, a few of these old relics enjoyed a new lease of life, when they were handed over to the Canadian Army for training. The remainder went for scrap.

The British Mk VIIIs had an even more ignominious end. The Ricardo-engined vehicles were transported to Wool by rail from NBL's factory a few months after the Armistice. Their only journey on their own tracks was the drive from the station to Bovington Camp when some difficulty was experienced due to faulty valve timing. In the post-war wave of euphoria they were dumped among the other tanks which reposed at Bovington in those days on their return from France, awaiting mechanical attention which they never received. Gradually they went for scrap, just one vehicle being retained when examples of each type used in the First World War were kept to form the nucleus of the RAC Tank Museum at Bovington.

Pigeon Post! The early tanks sent messages back to HQ (with luck) by carrier pigeon. Here one is released. Radio had rendered this idea obsolete by the war's end.

The Renault Tank

The Renault BS was an early self-propelled gun model with large turret and short 75 mm gun.

During the First World War the French were not so successful as the British in evolving heavy tanks, but they did make a major contribution to development of the tank by way of their eminently successful light tanks. The design which emanated from French thinking was revolutionary in many ways, and it adopted the now normally accepted tank lay-out right from the start – that is a traversing turret on the hull top and the hull itself divided into three sections, from front to rear, driving compartment, fighting compartment, and engine room. The majority of tank designs produced since then have featured such a layout.

Colonel (later General) Jean Baptiste Estienne was the 'father' of French tanks. Serving with the artillery on the Western Front in 1915, Estienne came to the same sort of conclusions as Swinton and the other British tank pioneers. Estienne was an imaginative man who had already pioneered the use of aircraft for artillery 'spotting' as early as 1909. At the Battle of the Marne in September 1914, he observed to fellow officers 'Whoever shall first be able to make land ironclads armed and equipped will have won the war'.

Estienne, like Swinton, saw in the Holt artillery tractor the basis of an armoured 'land-

FT 17 tanks lead the French Victory Parade in Paris in 1919. The leading machines are 1918 production models with the rounded turret and 37mm gun.

Why the tanks based on Holt-type suspension were unsuccessful. This view shows one of the French St Chamond heavy tanks catching its nose on the parapet as it attempts to cross quite a shallow ditch. The FT 17, like the British tanks, had a superior 'all round' track layout which prevented this.

ship', given the fitting of an armoured body. He wrote to General Joffre, the French C-in-C and asked to see him about '... employing mobile armoured constructions for the purpose of assuring the progress of the infantry, with a mechanical traction capable of conveying infantry through or over obstacles, under fire, with arms and baggage and with guns, at the speed of nearly 7 kmh.' Estienne quoted a budget of ten million francs for a six month 'crash' programme providing such vehicles for an attack on a 20-mile front.

Joffre sent Estienne to Paris in order to sound out industrialists about production of such vehicles. Louis Renault was first approached, but he declined to become involved due to lack of experience with crawler track vehicle production. The Schneider firm were more promising. They were French representatives for the Holt company of America and had already been involved in making an armoured version of the Baby Holt agricultural tractor, though this had proved unsatisfactory as a means of cutting through enemy barbed wire. Estienne worked with the chief engineer of Schneider to design a tank which fulfilled all his original requirements. The resulting vehicle, with 37mm gun, was known as a 'Char d'Assaut' – the Schneider CA. The first of these entered service in late 1916 and they saw action at Chemin des Dames in April 1917. The design proved unsatisfactory by comparison with the British heavy tank design. Because the Schneider still retained the low tractor-like track layout it was unstable and top-heavy. Its trench-crossing performance was poor and, in short, it lacked the fundamental features of overall tracks and all-round firepower which the British tanks possessed.

Similar short-comings imposed limitations on the other main French tank design, the Char St Chamond. Also on a Holt-type tractor chassis, this vehicle was designed by the French Service Technique Auto-mobile and had a petrol-electric motor and a boxy, rather unwieldy, superstructure.

Having taken a hand in designing the Schneider tank, Estienne now went on to plan a light tank specifically for close support of infantry – a small tank with machine gun armament. For this he returned to Renault, who now expressed an interest and assisted in the design. By December 1916 a model was completed. The lack of a gun of heavy calibre caused controversy among the 'Committee for Special Artillery' (the Commission set up to co-ordinate tank development) but Estienne's argument prevailed and a first order for 150 vehicles placed with Renault. Trials in April 1917 led to orders for 1000, though the demand for a larger calibre gun – later actually incorporated as a design variant – was conditional on the order.

By September 1917 orders in hand totalled 3500 and further contractors were called in to help Renault. Eventually Renault, Berliet, Somua and Delauny-Belleville were all engaged in tank production and the Renault FT 17 became a major service type.

Delays were experienced due to the new production techniques. One of the problems was the fabrication of cast turrets in armour plate. To overcome this, and speed production, an octagonal turret was designed of flat armour plates. The first 100 vehicles were completed with this turret and it was used also in subsequent production. After design work was completed on the turret, it was realized that, with

An octagonal fabricated turret was used on the first 100 vehicles, and on some other models. The two on the right here have the 37 mm gun, while the example on the left has the Hotchkiss 8 mm machine gun.

modifications to the mantlet, it was possible to mount a machine gun in the same turret. These versions were produced armed either with a 37mm gun or a machine gun as well as an un-armed signal vehicle.

Renault Models

General Estienne also conceived a fourth model which mounted a 75mm S gun on the same chassis. Production orders for this were placed in February 1918.

The French Army began to take delivery of production FT 17 vehicles early in 1918. In February 1918 there were 4000 light tanks on order and the breakdown between the four models was machine gun tanks 1000: 37mm gun tanks 1830; signal tanks 200 and 75mm gun tanks 970. The order for 970 75mm gun tanks also included a number of experimental types.

The FT 17

The hull of the FT 17 light duty tank was a simple armoured box narrowing towards the rear. Unlike the Schneider and St. Chamond, it did not have a chassis, the hull carrying the engine and running gear, characteristic of the majority of subsequent post-war tank designs. The engine, a 35bhp Renault unit, was at the rear. Unlike the early British tanks, which relied on gravity feed, the petrol supply was pumped from two petrol tanks with a total capacity of 22 gallons. The transmission included Renault cone clutches and a Renault gearbox, with four forward speeds and one reverse. The motor was started manually, either inside or outside the vehicle. The water coolant was pumped through a conventional tube radiator. Access to the engine was through panels at the hull rear.

The fighting and driving compartment occupied the front of the vehicle. It was entered

through two hatches which formed the glacis plate. A rear escape hatch was fitted on the prototype at the rear of the turret. This was changed to double doors on production vehicles. The driver sat in the front of the vehicle immediately below the access hatches. His seat was at floor level with a simple canvas back. His view was provided by three slots and an opening shutter, while his controls included a gear lever on the right and steering levers on either side. The gunner's position was in the turret at the centre of the vehicle, where he could stand or sit on a small adjustable seat.

The turret was carried on a bearing race which the gunner could turn manually. It could be locked by a brake. The turret had a small dome which could be tilted open to give access to the fighting compartment. The circular rim on which the dome was mounted had five vision slits and formed a simple cupola. The fighting compartment was separated from the engine by a steel bulkhead with ventilation shutters which could be closed in case of fire. Ammunition was stored in the base of the turret and along the walls of the fighting compartment.

The tracks projected well forward of the vehicle, permitting it to cross the most difficult terrain; unlike the Schneider and St. Chamond tanks, it could easily mount vertical obstacles and climb in and out of shell holes and trenches. The driving sprocket was at the rear. Tracks were tensioned by the adaptable front idler wheels. The ground run of the track was supported by four sets of wheels, one of three and three of two. This assembly was mounted on a heavy longitudinal girder carried on leaf springs. The upper track run was carried by a rail with six small guide rollers. This rail was pivoted at the rear and tensioned upwards against the track by a coil spring at the front.

Steering was by the simple conventional method of declutching and braking the transmission to the tracks on either side through the steering levers. A removable 'tail' was fitted at the rear of the vehicle to increase its effective length for trench crossing. The tank could easily be transported on trucks or trailers, a major factor in conserving track life and moving units quickly to a combat zone. In technical terms the Renault FT 17 was in advance of the British heavy tanks.

On the signal tank the turret was replaced by a rectangular armoured cupola. It had a double exit door at the rear, an opening cupola on top and a large observation slot in front. The vehicle also had a periscope. It carried a radio operator, observer and driver/mechanic.

The 75mm gun tank was the first self-propelled gun to be put into service. The proto-type had the gun mounted in a front compartment and the driver's position was moved above the engine compartment under a small cupola. It had a crew of three, including two gunners. The production version differed from the prototype to simplify production. The original hull was used unchanged and only the turret was altered. The turret was made up of flat armoured plates with only seven sides. The escape hatch was moved to the left side and a turret bustle projected at the rear to give room for the recoil of the 75 mm S gun.

First four FT 17 vehicles were delivered in September 1917. It was not until March 1918, however, that they were passed to the Army. The first unit was 501 Regiment de Chars de Combat which had three battalions. The first battle in which Renault FT 17 light tanks were involved was on May 31, 1918, at the Retz Forest. This was during the German summer offensive and the light tanks, although committed in small groups, did well and supported the infantry in checking the advance. On July 18th 480 FTs were concentrated in the French counter-offensive at Soissons where they broke the German line in the initial attack without artillery preparation.

To keep the tanks in the field, maintenance workshops were established at Bourron in May 1918. This base gained a good reputation for its speed and efficiency in keeping the FT 17s in fighting trim.

The Renault FT was one of the most widely used tanks in the world in the inter war years. A major user was the US Army, for whom a special version was built in America. When the Americans entered the First World War and formed a tank corps, their heavy battalions were equipped with British heavy tanks, and the light battalions with Renault FTs. Twenty battalions were scheduled and it was planned to build 1 200 of these, later to be increased to 4400 vehicles in America. In fact, only 950 were built by the end of the war. Under the designation M1917, this 6 tonner served the US Army until the 1930s. In 1940 some were shipped to the Canadian Army. The American-built version was considerably re-engineered for production in America. For example it had to be replanned in non-metric measurements.

Spain, China, Finland, Japan, Belgium, Brazil, Holland, Poland, and Czechoslovakia purchased vehicles from France in the 1920s. The Russians built a licence version, which they later developed. This vehicle, designated KS, was popularly known as the 'Russki Reno'. The Italians similarly built the Renault FT under licence and developed it, with a few improvements, as the Fiat 3000. As a final irony, many Renault 17s still served with the French Army in 1940 and these fell into German hands on the capitulation of France and were used by the German Army in Europe until 1945.

Six ton M1917 37mm

The United States' version of the FT 17 was the M1917 Six Tonner. These examples are in service with the Canadian Army in 1940, having been sold at nominal value from obsolete stocks to help Canada's war effort when British tanks were in short supply. The nearest vehicle has a 37mm gun, the others machine guns.

The Small Tanks

Light Tank Mk VIB was one of the later Vickers-built light tanks in British service. Cadet officers are training in this one in August 1940.

Side and front views of the Morris-Martel one-man light tank, an official prototype built around Martel's ideas.

After the ending of the First World War there was a fertile period in Great Britain, when light tanks and so-called 'tankettes' were produced in some numbers. This initiated a trend to light fighting vehicles which was taken up by most armed powers. Small light tanks enjoyed a vogue and lent themselves to the reduced defence spending of the inter-war period. They were cheap to produce, simple to operate, and could, in theory, at least be justified in military terms. They were ideal for colonial 'police' work and border patrol, for instance, and quite adequate for training troops in tank warfare.

Much of the thinking behind the idea came from the experience of tank warfare on the Western Front in 1916–18. When tanks were still only available in relatively limited numbers, tank men dreamed of the day when the entire battlefield would be filled with 'swarms of armoured skirmishers' to use the words of the French pioneer, General Estienne. His inspiration, the little Renault FT 17, was, as we have

seen, widely admired and in peacetime years it was licence-built or purchased by many other countries. In America Henry Ford produced a tiny 'two man tank' which was based on the automotive parts of the Model T 'Tin Lizzy' but the war was over before many could be made.

In the early 1920s, when British defence spending was cut to a bare minimum, one officer of the Tank Corps, Major Giffard Le Q. Martel, revived the small tank idea by building a tiny one man tank at home in his garage, using readily available motor car parts. The War Office was sufficiently impressed with his work to order a few one-man and two-man tanks to Martel's design, entrusting the work to two motor car manufacturers, Morris and Crossley.

Concurrently an ex-officer, Captain J.V.Carden, had designed a similar small vehicle, using Ford Model T engine and transmission, with a simple track made of conveyor belt chain. Carden contacted Martel and was put on to the

War Office who sanctioned further development. Carden managed a garage owned by another ex-officer, Captain Vivian Loyd, and together they formed the Carden Loyd company to carry out the work. For the 1926 Commonwealth Conference the firm was able to demonstrate three vehicles. The original Carden Loyd Tankette Mk I had a simple open box body with front sprocket drive, brake drum steering, and rear radiator forming the back of the body. The tracks were unsprung and the driver sat astride the Ford engine in motor-cyclist fashion. A partly traversing front shield protected the driver and had a machine gun embrasure. The Tankette Mk I* was similar but had a pair of wheels outboard of the tracks, and a rear steerable wheel, so that the vehicle could run in tricycle fashion on its wheels, thus conserving the very short track life (80 miles). Chain drive from the sprockets drove the front wheels and the axles were carried on crank axles which could be raised or dropped when it was desired to switch from wheels to tracks. The two-man tankette had a widened body (allowing two men to sit abreast).

In 1927 came refined models, the Mk II and Mk III, essentially like the Mk I and Mk I* respectively, except that the suspension was vastly improved, with spring girder frame carrying rubber-tyred bogies and a redesigned track with a 300-mile life. The Carden Loyd Tankette Mk IV combined these new features with the body of the 1926 two-man vehicle, so that the crew now became driver and machine gunner. Eight Mk IVs were ordered for the Tank Corps and these went into service in 1928.

At about the same time, the big firm of Vickers-Armstrong Ltd, who were already building medium tanks, acquired Carden Loyd Ltd and its two principals. The next tankettes produced were the Mk V and Mk V* which introduced improved tracks, a larger steerable rear wheel and, in the V*, leaf springs in the suspension. Late in 1928 came the Mk VI which was the definitive production version and enjoyed huge success. Over 300 were built for the British Army and there were many variants. These included mortar carriers, an anti-tank gun tractor (with tracked limber and gun carriage), machine gun carriers, and a 47mm self-propelled gun. Variations in the design included armoured head covers, canvas canopies, and several types of front shield.

Vickers sold the design energetically abroad and Canada, Bolivia, Chile, Japan, Holland and Thailand were among purchasers. In addition licence production agreements were signed with major powers, and, with only minor design variations, substantially the same vehicle was built by Italy (L29), France (Latil N), Czecho-

slovakia (Skoda MV4/T), Russia (T27), and Poland. The Italians developed the CV 3/33, the French the Renault UE, and the Poles the TK, all from the same basic design, but slightly enlarged. In America the Marmon-Herrington company built a series of small tanks, the idea for these coming from the Carden Loyd concept, although the design was different.

The story did not end there, for Vickers developed the Mk VI tankette in two directions.

From top to bottom Carden Loyd Mk II tankette, Carden Loyd Mk I* (wheel and track) tankette, and Carden Loyd Mk V, showing rear wheel.

35

First they produced a succession of Light Dragons (artillery tractors) and infantry carriers, a series culminating in the Bren Gun Carrier and Universal Carrier family of the Second World War. Then Vickers put a light turret on a tankette to produce a so-called 'patrol tank'. Two versions were built, one with the original type of suspension – which now proved too light – and the next with larger road wheels and helical springs. For commercial sale overseas Vickers built numerous variations on the light tank theme, continuing up to the outbreak of war. In the meantime the machine that had been produced by Vickers as the 'light tank Mk VII' in their original tankette series was developed for the British Army into the Light Tank series Mks I to VI which saw service up to 1942. To meet service requirements, the original basic design changed beyond all recognition and the vehicle became bulkier and heavier, with heavy machine gun armament. There were dozens of models and variations and some of the types are illustrated. The Mk VI vehicles of 1939 were three-man tanks, with cupola in the turret and side-mounted engine – a complete tank in miniature. The design inspired the newly-formed Wehrmacht too – in the early 1930s the Germans purchased some Vickers carriers (as 'agricultural tractors') and based their own light tank design, the Panzerkampfwagen I, closely on the Vickers chassis, suspension, and layout.

Far left A French development of the Carden Loyd tankette idea, the Renault UE infantry carrier (foreground). Note the armoured 'lobster shell' head covers.

Left One of several Vickers commercial light tank designs, typical of those sold commercially to many small nations in the 1930s.

Below Light tanks formed a great proportion of Britain's meagrely equipped armoured forces at the beginning of the Second World War. Here are the two most numerous types in service, a Mk VIA (*right*) and a Mk VIB, on patrol near the Libyan border in 1940, before the Italian invasion of Egypt.

Right Vickers 6 ton light tank was one of the most influential of all tank designs in the 1930s. The Model A twin turret variant is shown here. Note the simple suspension.

Below: Russian-built version of the Vickers 6 tonner saw service in vast numbers well into the 1940s. A T-26B with single turret and 47mm gun is followed by a twin-turreted T-26A.

Bottom Inspired by the Vickers light tank designs, but not directly related, was the German Panzer-kampfwagen I, shown here in Norway in 1940.

The end of the light tank idea came suddenly in 1940–41, when the early tank campaigns of the Second World War – in France and in the Western Desert – proved that light tanks were easy victims to aircraft and anti-tank guns, while their reconnaissance role could be carried out as effectively and more easily by armoured cars. The light tank disappeared from service with almost indecent haste and those that survived had only brief careers as training vehicles or other specialist types.

One other Vickers light tank is worthy of note – the Vickers 6 tonner. This was produced purely as a commercial venture in 1928 and was in production for overseas sale until 1939. Bolivia, Bulgaria, China, Estonia, Finland, Greece, Japan, Poland, Portugal, Romania, Russia, and Siam were major purchasers. One vehicle went to America in 1931 and the layout of the combat cars and light tanks developed in the 1930s (Chapter 5) was based quite closely on the Vickers design. The Russians built the design under licence, and as the T-26 this was a major service type which saw service well into the Second World War.

Two basic models were made. The first, Type A, had two machine gun turrets side by side. Type B had a single large turret with 47mm gun – or any variation demanded by the purchaser. The 6 tonner was a simple machine of riveted construction and with sturdy spring suspension and short pitch tracks. It had an air-cooled 80bhp Armstrong-Siddeley engine and a top speed of 22mph. A fairly novel feature for its time was a firewall between the engine and the fighting compartment. While the Vickers 6 tonner was, perhaps, one of the world's least memorable tanks – it looked dull and plain, unlike the tankettes – it was numerically of great importance and it had more influence on future design and ideas than any of the tankettes.

Christie Tanks

While Swinton, Wilson and the other tank pioneers were working hard in Britain, in America another original thinker who was to influence future tank design to a considerable extent in the years up to 1940 and beyond was at work. This was J. Walter Christie, another automotive engineer who became interested in fighting vehicle design in the early years of the First World War. Before America entered the war, its automotive industry was a supplier of trucks and cars in vast numbers to Britain and France.

Christie built a self-propelled carriage for a 3 in gun on the chassis of one of the trucks built by his firm, Front Drive Motor Company. The US Army bought the vehicle from Christie for $7800 in December 1916. The vehicle was of no great military merit but it gave Christie an entrée to the military authorities and made him become interested in the problems and requirements for military vehicles.

Christie's next vehicle, a self-propelled 8 in howitzer Mk VI gun carriage (1918 model) of which four were ordered in December 1917 for $60000, was radically different – it was the forerunner of all Christie military vehicles. It could run on wheels or tracks and had a top speed of 16 mph, which was remarkable for its day, beyond military requirements then envisaged.

This encouraged Christie to continue designing SP guns and he produced three more models by 1920. The 1918 model had already started Christie on tank design. The gun carrier prototype on proving trials at Camp Charles, South Carolina, in September 1917, demonstrated a good cross country performance and, with British tanks by then in France, Christie was encouraged to pursue tank design.

He won an order for the first Christie tank (M1919) and for a rebuild (M1921), at a total cost of $82000.

Tank M1919

When the M1919 was delivered to the Army in November 1919, it proved in many ways a less effective vehicle than the gun carriage which inspired its design. It was rather quickly assembled and proved mechanically unreliable. In his attempt to enclose the vehicle with armour, Christie had left the engine and transmission inaccessible and the fighting compartment small and badly ventilated. Its worst fault lay in the suspension. The volute centre bogie, with only two small road wheels at each side, offered insufficient weight distribution over the lower run of the track. The front idler and rear drive wheels, which carried the main load, were unsprung. With a 120 bhp 6 cylinder engine the 13·5 ton vehicle was also considerably underpowered, by Christie's later standards, and achieved only 7 mph.

Christie set out to correct these faults and M1921, built on the same basic chassis and hull,

Top Cruiser Tank Mk IV was a fairly successful British derivation of the original Christie tank M1932 design. These vehicles are on exercises in England in April 1941.

Above Christie's M1921 design had pivoted sprung bogies which led to his later definitive suspension system. Note the 57 mm gun mounted in the nose instead of in the turret, another Christie characteristic.

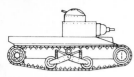

Christie 57mm

had sprung front wheels and much larger and heavier centre bogies. Showing the trend of his future design thinking, he also omitted the high, exposed turret and brought the 6pdr (57mm) main armament to a forward-facing ball mounting, leaving the driver mounted amidships, protected by a small barbette turret, slotted for all-round vision. This arrangement was well ahead of its time, foreshadowing the German tank destroyers of the Second World War and the Swedish 'S' tank of the 1960s in layout. By the time M1921 appeared US military chiefs had broken up the Tank Corps and reduced the status of tanks to the infantry support role manned by the infantry – and there was, in any case, a severe curtailment of defence spending.

Christie turned to designing amphibians. Once again he succeeded brilliantly – and also failed. In an effort to attract attention to his M1922 amphibian he plunged it into the Hudson River on December 6, 1922, drove it across at five knots against a fast tide and climbed out up a 20ft rock revetment on to the New York Central railroad tracks.

The publicity resulting from this achievement seemed to pay off; Christie won an order for six amphibious vehicles from the US Marine Corps and another was purchased by Japan. In 1923 a Christie amphibian made the first ship-to-shore assault trial from USS *Wisconsin* off Puerto Rico. It demonstrated with uncanny accuracy the use of a similar type of tracked armoured amphibian (LVT (A)) which was to become almost commonplace in the Second World War. However this was still very much in the future and Christie received no more orders and the project was dropped.

Christie had a lean time in the mid-1920s and had to rest content with improved model amphibians and paper projects. However, in 1928, the US Government completed payment of $100000 patent rights and Christie at once invested in a new company, US Wheel Track Layer Corporation, and a new tank design which could run on either tracks or wheels, the M1928. This was the forerunner of M1931, adopted by the US Army as the Medium T3. In this year an Experimental Mechanized Force, based on the contemporary British idea of 1927, was set up at Fort Meade, Maryland. Christie hurried to produce a tank, but within three months, the force was disbanded because it had no suitable vehicles. The M1928 did not go on test before a special board of assessors convened by the US Army Ordnance Department until October 1930. The test ordered by the Board included a 200 miles road run on wheels, 140 miles across country on tracks to be completed in seven hours, fording a 3ft deep stream and climbing a 35 degree slope from standing start without grousers. The Christie vehicle also ran an obstacle course of 8in logs, turned its 18ft length in an 18ft roadway and pushed through a previously impassable bog. The maximum speeds registered were: road (wheeled) 70mph; cross country (tracked) 42·5mph; rough terrain 30mph. On the basis of this remarkable performance the Board reported three months later: 'The basic features embodied in this tank are sound . . . their development will lead to the securing of a tank which will meet the needs of the Army. . . . The Board recommends the immediate acceptance of this tank'. In March 1931 an order for five Christie tanks was announced and Christie set up a plant at Linden, New Jersey, to manufacture the T3. Delivery of these vehicles commenced in September 1931 at the basic price of $34500 each less turret, armament, radio and engine.

By any standards the M1928, the M1930, and the production version, Medium Tank T3, was a remarkable and revolutionary design, a far cry from the lumbering great 'landships' of little more than a decade earlier.

The M1928 and the Medium T3 were closely similar in basic chassis design as were all subsequent tanks, combat cars, and gun motors designed directly by J.Walter Christie. They were rear-engined, rear-wheel drive vehicles with high power weight ratio – in the M1928 turretless, unarmed chassis as high as 39·3bhp/ton – with four large rubber cushion-tyred road wheels 2ft 3½in diameter, each independently suspended on lever arms, pivoted on the hull side and supported by heavy coil springs. The Christie patent suspension was the key to the high speed and good overland performance. In essence the road wheels were carried on three vertical springs contained by web girder brackets within the double-skinned hull sides and with casts protruding above the deck plates. This clumsy vertical arrangement was dispensed with on later models but it allowed a vertical wheel displacement of 14in. The forward road wheels, which were steerable for road running, were suspended on a horizontal spring contained in a sleeve which ran back through the converging nose side plates.

The original T3 (Christie construction) was powered by a standard Liberty V-12 engine officially rated at 338bhp at 1400rpm. However, a maximum rpm of 2500 was obtainable with this engine, on which Christie did considerable additional modification work, and the T3 installation is known to have reached a rating of 387bhp at times. The power was so great that it would permit speeds far beyond those of any previous tank and, across country, it was almost beyond the endurance of the crew. Thus the Christie vehicles were dramatic, if not entirely practical. The T3, fully equipped in service weighed 10·5 tons, compared with 8·6 tons of the bare M1931 chassis, and the maximum cross country speed specified in the Ordnance data sheets was 27·3 mph.

Novel features of the T3 and other Christie vehicles were the tracks and unusual sprocket drive. The die-stamped steel track shoes were large, measuring approximately 10 sq in and hinged by steel pins which could readily be knocked out. The centre of alternate shoes carried a large 7 in tongue which engaged roller bars in the drive sprocket wheel and also guided the tracks between the split tyres of the road wheels. This ensured that the tracks were held at high speeds and during violent manoeuvres. However, the wide shoes passing round the small sprocket and idler wheels suffered violent angular movement at the hinges, rapidly wearing out the track pins. Nevertheless the Christie tracks were light and easily handled. Two men could remove tracks and stow them on the special racks situated above the track run in 30 minutes.

Anatomy of the T3

The T3 carried a crew of three: driver, gunner and commander. The interior was divided nominally into driving, fighting and engine compartments although there were no bulkheads and the huge engine and transmission installation occupied all the interior aft of the turret ring. The driver entered by two butterfly doors which also formed his square, armoured barbette on the sharp pointed glacis plate. Access to the fighting compartment was through a simple, circular turret roof hatch. The driver sat with his feet well forward in the nose. His controls included a Ford Model A steering wheel when the tank ran on road wheels and two track clutch/brake control levers for steering on tracks. He had a conventional accelerator and gear lever. The instrument panel on his left carried an ignition switch, self-starter button, oil pressure gauge, petrol gauge, speedometer and tachometer. The turret on a 360 degree traverse bearing ring was rotated by a hand crank and spur gear.

The engine was flanked by large radiators and fans at either side taking in cooling air through two armoured louvres in the deck. A large flywheel at the rear, with conventional ring gear and starter motor, carried seven large fan blades which forced air out through louvres in the hull back plate.

The transmission of the M1928, M1931 (T3) and a subsequent export model, the M1932 (British A13E1) was transversely mounted and extremely simple, being designed for the high power/weight ratio that was achieved. Engine power was transmitted through a heavy steel plate clutch and bevel gear to the transverse input shaft. The output shaft carried sliding pinions for gear change. There was one reverse and four forward speeds. Overall reduction in the lowest gear was 28:1 – about 2½ times the normal figure for vehicles in the weight class at that time and which further enhanced the phenomenal Christie climb performance. Conversely, in top forward speed the reduction from engine to sprocket was only 3·9:1. The outer ends of the output shaft carried multiple steering clutches integrated with the track brakes for steering, stopping and parking. In the first five T3 vehicles delivered the final drive from output shaft to sprocket was by chain. A train of gears was fitted in T3E1 (see below) and the M1932, however.

Both pictures Medium Tank T3 (Christie Model M1931) in service status, with the 67th Armor Battn in 1932. Infantry and vehicles are seen in action during the annual 'war games'.

41

Top M1937 was one of Christie's fastest vehicles and could sustain a speed of 60mph.
Above M1928 had a nose-mounted gun. This basic design, but with a turret, developed into the M1931 for the US Army.

Variants

Nine M1931 vehicles were built and their history was somewhat chequered. The first five ordered by the US Army were originally designated Medium Tank T3. The next two were ordered by the Polish government, which defaulted on payment and these were then adapted by the US Army as the T3E1. The two further chassis

built were sold under licence to the USSR becoming Bystrokhodnyi Tank (fast tank) BT1, as recounted later. M1931 vehicle numbers 1, 3, 4 and 5 were delivered to the US Cavalry at Fort Knox in 1932. Because the Cavalry were still officially not permitted tanks the designation was changed to T1 Combat Car. Numbers 2, 6 and 7, delivered to the Infantry, carried the true Medium Tank T3 designation and were named 'Tornado', 'Hurricane' and 'Cyclone'.

The T3 was armed with one 37mm turret gun with a coaxial ·30 calibre machine gun. The Cavalry Combat Car T1 had only one ·50 calibre machine gun. In 1932 the Infantry ordered five additional T3 Medium Tanks, but by this time Christie had quarrelled with the Army again and these were built by American LaFrance and designated T3E2. This vehicle was fitted with LaFrance engines, had an octagonal flat-sided turret and weighed 14·2 tons. A further variant with controlled differential steering was built by this company in 1936 and designated T3E3. Another project, the T1E3, was planned to have a Cummins diesel engine, but it was never taken up.

Walter Christie had always had somewhat

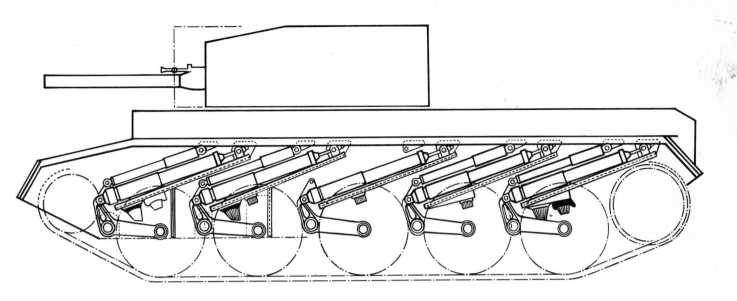

strained relationships with the US Army. Like most men of genius he was wilful and single-minded. He had his own ideas of what a tank should do, what his own designs could do, and how well they were suited to what he envisaged would be the style of future tank warfare. But Christie's ideas were way ahead of the military command's, which were nothing if not very conservative. He quarrelled with the Army command over their requirements – notably the insistence on the conventional turret which gave a high silhouette, for Christie postulated a low-mounted barbette in the nose.

As a result of the various quarrels with the military command, all subsequent vehicles based on Christie patent features were designed and built elsewhere. They included the Cavalry's Combat Car T2 and the Infantry Tank T4. The latter was designed by the Ordnance Department at Rock Island Arsenal in 1933 and 16 were built by 1936, when, most unfortunately, this extremely promising vehicle – remarkably like the BT series by this time being mass-produced in Russia – was dropped both for economy reasons and, bluntly, lack of appreciation and foresight. The US went to war in 1941 with no Christie vehicles.

In the US Army the T3 was used mainly for infantry training. The tactical possibilities opened up by the T3 were not followed up, and ironically enough the Russians were left to make the running.

Meanwhile Christie himself forged ahead designing and building experimental tanks which were known as his airborne series. By this time he was becoming more and more obsessed with speed and with the notion that his vehicles should have sufficient speed over the ground to evade attacking aircraft or to be delivered from moving aircraft at touch down speeds in excess of 60mph. By 1936–37 he was using modified Curtiss Wright D-12 engines uprated to 450bhp

in an effort to achieve his aims.

Christie, then, remained something of a prophet without honour in his own country and it was left to two other major powers to exploit his ideas more fully. In the event designs based on Christie's patents played a major part in the Second World War – not with the United States Army, but with those of the Soviet Union and Britain. And of these two it was the Russians who made the fastest and most effective progress.

The Russian Developments

By the early 1930s the Red Army had adopted the mobile war philosophies of the British armour theorists of the time, Fuller and Liddell Hart, and were able to translate theories into reality by exploiting the efforts of Christie, and his 'fast tanks'.

In December 1929 a special commission, headed by the Director of Mechanization and Motorization of the Red Army set out on a tour of Europe and the USA. Their mission was to inspect available armoured vehicles under development or test which might be considered suitable for the new tactical roles envisaged by the Red Army. In the USA they were greatly impressed by the new wheel/track design built by Christie. The suggestion was made at high level of contacting Christie and offering him a substantial sum of money to assist in the development of tanks in the USSR but nothing came of the proposal. However, during 1931 two Christie M1931 (T3) tanks were purchased from the USA and tested extensively by the Russians at one of their tank depots to determine their suitability for use by the Soviet Army. The results of these tests were favourable, and in the same year the War Council of the USSR ordered design work to be started on a home-built version of the Christie model. Manufacture of this first model (BT-1) commenced

Typical Christie suspension layout showing the springs and shock dampers relative to the wheels and hull side. This vehicle is a British Cromwell of 1944.

in May 1931, at the Komintern factory in Kharkov and it was completed by June. A simplified version of the tank was designed. Two further prototypes were then built which became known as the BT-2. These were completed by September 3. In effect the Russian BT design (Bystrochodniya Tankov – fast tank) was a very close copy of Christie's original, adapted to suit Russian engineering ability. Following completion the two tanks were subjected to stiff trials and later, on October 7, they participated in the parade in the Red Square.

Manufacturing facilities for the mass production of BT tanks were ordered and became an essential part of the Soviet Second Five Year Plan. Production was initially concentrated at the Komintern Factory, although eventually BTs were in production at 32 major tank plants. The Special Commission which had travelled abroad had also visited Germany where they purchased the licence from BMW to produce the M17 engine. This engine was subsequently adopted to power BT tanks.

Anatomy of the BT

The general construction of the BT tank closely resembled that of the original Christie vehicle and had the engine and transmission at the rear.

The turret was identical to that used on the original Christie tank and was mounted centrally on the forward part, and the driver was seated centrally at the extreme front. As with the original Christie tank, the BT could run on either wheels or tracks, a change from one state to the other taking about 30 minutes.

When running on tracks, the chain sprocket on each side of the driving wheel was replaced by four rollers which drove the tracks via the driving lugs carried on alternate track plates. When running on wheels, the power was transmitted from the main driving wheels to the solid steering bogie wheels (in contrast to the original Christie vehicles which had the rear pair of bogie wheels driven) through a chain drive (the hollow forged-steel track plates being carried on shelves running along the sides of the hull).

In the tracked form the vehicle was steered by the conventional clutch and brake method. The rear pair of bogie wheels carried about one-third of the tank weight; thus the tractive effort of the tank when moving on wheels was considerably less than when running on tracks. Wheeled operation was intended only for hard-surfaced roads, since on soft going the driving wheels would dig into the soil and spin.

Although the BT incorporated this facility for running on either wheels or tracks throughout its period of use with the Soviet Army, the Russians rarely utilized the tank in the wheeled form. This was due to the time required for the

44

change-over operation, which was not always available in combat conditions.

The main advantage of the BT was not that it was a wheel/track vehicle but that it could develop a high speed on tracks, thus making it capable of carrying out long range sorties and moving quickly about a combat zone. High-speed BT tanks demonstrated conclusively the feasibility of fast moving tank units during training and manoeuvres. There were, however, complaints of a tendency to shed tracks, especially if turns were at all abrupt and not handled smoothly.

In the original Christie design extensive use had been made of electric-arc welding, but the early Soviet BT models were rivetted throughout. The performance of the tank was excellent, resulting from the high power-to-weight ratio. The BT1 was powered by a 400bhp Russian version of the Liberty V type used in the original Christie tanks. The Christie suspension provided a remarkably stable gun platform, but it necessitated a double-wall construction – there being an inner skin of 7·5mm – and therefore displaced a lot of room within the tank. This suspension was also vulnerable, intricate, and difficult to maintain in the field.

Unofficially the BT tank was called the 'Betka' (Beetle) and, due to its three-man crew, also the 'Tri Tankista' (Three Tanker). The basic models adopted for service were the BT2, BT5, BT7, and BT7M.

BT Models

The first model, the BT1, was armed with two machine guns in the turret. Trials with this tank proved the turret and armament installation to be below requirements and production was halted after only one vehicle had been built. A second model, designated BT2 (or Christie-Russki 1931) was constructed during late 1931. This model closely resembled the BT1, but had a turret of a new design; the prototype, like the BT1, was armed with two machine guns, but production models mounted a 37mm M1930 tank gun and one machine gun.

The 37mm gun was aimed with a shoulder support, and the 7·62mm machine-gun was located separately, in a ball-mounting to the right of the gun. The BT2 was approved for production in January 1932.

Even though the adoption of the BT2 marked a significant advance in Soviet tank development, this model was still improved upon. Two further variants, BT3 and BT4, were developed to investigate various armament combinations. Whereas the BT2 had mantlet guards and spoked wheels, the BT3 had a slightly modified turret and solid pressed-steel wheels. In place of the 37mm gun a 45mm anti-tank gun was mounted. A few examples of this third model were built.

The BT4 was an unsuccessful attempt to produce an infantry version of the BT equipped with the twin turret arrangement of the T-26A light tank series; only a few prototypes were made.

These first four BT models had a power-to-weight ratio of 35bhp/ton. This high power-to-weight ratio enabled the employment of a gearbox with four forward gears and one reverse.

Towards the end of 1932 a better BT model was specified with the provision of more powerful armament, a coaxial mounting for the machine gun, the provision of radio equipment, and more room in the turret and fighting compartment. Designated BT5, this further model mounted a 45mm M1932 tank gun with coaxial machine gun mounting in an improved turret with radio equipment. The 45mm armour-piercing shot of the M1932 gun had a muzzle velocity of 2350fps – which provided a firepower greater than that of all foreign light tanks, and certain medium tanks, right up to the outbreak of the Second World War. The BT5 also had a more powerful engine, the Soviet designed M5 12-cylinder aircraft model, specially adapted for tank use.

The original BT5 turret was cylindrical, but later models had a rear overhang. Twin optical sights were fitted (telescope and periscope). Another major change was the adoption of stronger suspension. The armour remained unaltered. A commander's model provided with radio and designated BT5 (V), was also produced with a frame aerial around the turret roof.

The BT5 went into production at the end of 1932. It proved an extremely successful application of the Christie design, and utilized the link-plate track later used for the T-34 tank. The BT5 became a standard model and remained in service until 1941. Apart from the turret, the general arrangement of this tank closely followed that of the BT1. The BT5 was first demonstrated during the large-scale exercises in the Byelorussian Military District in 1935. A version of the BT5 armed with a 76·2mm L/16·5 gun (and one or two machine guns), designated BT5A, was produced for use in second echelons as artillery fire support for assault tanks (Artilleriyskich Tank).

Engineers at the Kharkov factory designed a whole range of experimental BT variants for different roles. Two experimental special-purpose tanks were developed on the BT3 design: in 1937 a BT3 was converted to a bridge-layer with a crude wooden bridge that was folded over the turret and manually lifted forwards by the crew; a flame-throwing version produced in 1937–40 had the turret and armament of the

OT133 (T26C light flame-throwing tank). Bridging units in armoured formations received the BT-IT bridge-layer tank based on the BT5, whilst older vehicles were reworked as crane tanks (Podiemniya Tankov) for engineer units. Some BT tanks were fitted with smoke emitters (designated BT-DT), and others with emitters for poison gas, and could be used to lay a 'contaminated zone'. Some BTs were also provided with fascines for assault.

Further development of the BT tank resulted from the production of a powerful modern engine with increased fuel capacity, and led to the construction in 1935 of the BT7 (the BT6 never passed the planning stage). Eventually becoming the most numerous Soviet tank model of its time, the BT7 was greatly favoured by Soviet tank troops. BT7s first served in tactical exercises in the Ukraine during 1935 and again in Byelorussia during autumn 1936.

The success of operations involving tank units equipped with BT7s during the battles in the Khalkhin-Gol area of Manchuria in 1938, and of the march to western Byelorussia and the western Ukraine during the Soviet-German partition of Poland in September 1939, was made possible mainly by the high mobility and reliability of these tanks. The BT7 was used in Finland in 1940, and then against the Germans in 1941. The BT7 was powered by the new M17T engine (originally designed for aircraft

Top Russian BT-5, showing its appearance without tracks for road running on wheels. This model had a Russian-developed turret and 47mm gun.

Above BT-7s make an impressive fast run across Red Square, Moscow, in the 1940 May Day parade.

Below A BT-5 and infantry make a characteristic attack on German positions during the German invasion of Russia in 1941.

use), developing 450bhp at 1750rpm. It was also provided with a new steering system, transmission and suspension. A new clutch and stronger gearbox was designed, in which the forward gears were reduced to three. Also introduced was a stabilizing system to ensure equivalent braking torque in both forward and reverse motion. The fuel capacity was increased to provide a greater range of operation and a small-pitch track was fitted. The early production models had the old cylindrical turret of the BT5. At the same time commanders' tanks had the turret of the BT5(V) with frame aerial and radio. Shortly after production was under way, however, a new improved conical turret (similar to that used on the T-26S tank) was introduced. The armour on this new turret was increased to 15mm. The hull front armour was also increased, from 13 to 22mm, but the side armour remained unaltered. The armour components of the hull and turret, formerly rivetted, were now electro-welded. The use of electric arc-welding increased the strength of the hull. The ammunition stowage for the 45mm gun was increased and a coaxial mounting was installed for the 7·62mm machine gun. Some vehicles were fitted with an additional machine gun in the rear of the turret and a machine gun for defence against low-flying aircraft.

A supporting artillery version of the BT7 was produced mounting a 76·2mm gun. This

vehicle, taken into service as the BT7A, fired an AP projectile having a muzzle velocity of 1190fps. A machine gun was located in a ball mounting to the right of the gun. The BT7A moved only on tracks. To provide a more stable firing platform the rear idler was removed and the track taken around the trailing rear road wheel.

Aside from the artillery versions of the BT5 and BT7 no other self-propelled mountings were adopted utilizing the BT hull and running gear. In December 1934, work was begun on a new medium tank, the T-29-5. This was a fast version of the T-28 with the original hull and

A BT-7 shows its ability to cope with difficult terrain on summer exercises in 1940. Note the twin horn periscopes on the turret top, and the simple vision slits.

turrets mounted on Christie (BT7) running gear, which incorporated the facility for travelling on wheels or tracks. Unlike the BT tank, when running on wheels the T-29-5 was driven on all four axles which greatly improved its mobility. It could attain a speed of 35mph on tracks, and 40mph on wheels. The overall weight of the T-29-5 was about 24 tons. A year later a further variant, the T-29, was built but neither passed the prototype stage.

In 1938 gun-laying in BT tanks was considerably improved with the introduction of a vertically stabilized sight (TOS) as well as the employment of an electric fuse primer.

From 1936 onwards M.I.Koshkin was the chief designer at the Kharkov factory which was the main producer of BT tanks, and he carried out extensive work on modernizing this vehicle. Among other new developments the BD-2 experimental diesel engine was tried out in a BT tank. The success of tests with the V-2 tank diesel engine in a BT5 tank prompted the design and manufacture during 1939 of a number of production model BT7M tanks – the first tanks with a powerful diesel engine. The BT7M (also known as the BT8) weighed 14·6 tons, mounted a 76·2mm gun and had several changes in hull and turret arrangement from the preceding tanks in the BT series: the glacis plate occupied the full width of the tank and was in the form of an inverted 'V'; a hull machine gun was installed next to the driver, and ball-mounted machine guns were located in each side of the turret. The turret, which mounted the 76·2mm gun in a rectangular mantlet, was a departure from the original BT tanks and more closely resembled that fitted to the T-28 medium. This last model in the BT series was eventually stripped of its facility for running without tracks. It was first publicly shown during the May Day review of 1938. Production of BT tanks was terminated during 1939–40 when the BT was replaced by the T-34.

British Developments

After the Russians it was the turn of the British to be impressed by Christie's designs. But the British came upon the potential of the Christie vehicles in a second-hand way – by witnessing the Russian BT tanks in service. In late 1936, Lt. Col. Giffard Le Q.Martel, the man who had helped pioneer the tankettes in the early 1920s, was appointed as the British Army's Assistant Director of Mechanization at a time when Hitler's Germany was re-arming and attention was being turned in Britain to the problem of re-equipping the ageing tank force.

In his official capacity, Martel attended the Red Army's Autumn Manoeuvres, where the BT tanks were put through their paces en masse, to impress the foreign military observers. Martel was highly impressed and wrote: 'The design of the fighting body is not very good but the performance of the machine is at least twice as good as the A9 (British Cruiser Mk I). The suspension is excellent. The maximum speed is at least 30mph, and it travels across average country at 20mph easily.... We saw several machines pass at 30mph over a prepared bank which had a vertical drop of 5 feet on the far side. The whole machine leapt through the air and cleared a 30 foot gap. There was no apparent damage to the suspension or the crew. The engine is an aircraft engine of some 300hp output... and the great advantage of using a really powerful engine is very apparent. This lighter type of medium tank is developed from the Christie tank which the Russians bought from America and fitted with their own engine and armament. It has one 37mm gun and one machine gun coaxial in the turret and I think 16mm armour basis. I think we should buy a Russian Christie at once to study the suspension.'

The A9 was at that time Britain's latest design which, in 1936, had been tested prior to going into production to replace the old Medium Mk I and Mk II tanks which had served since the 1920s. The A9 was built down to a price for economy reasons. Powered by an AEC bus engine, it was slow (about 15mph) and had a simple beam-type 'slow motion' suspension.

The British War Office acted with uncharacteristic speed and approved the purchase of a Christie vehicle, but from Christie himself rather than the Russians. Morris Commercial Cars Ltd. were appointed as government agents for the transaction and imported the vehicle – less the turret – as a 'tractor', the particular vehicle imported being M1932, the later version of the original 'fast tank' design. Christie himself came too.

Designated A13E1 in the British ordnance inventory, the tank was given exhaustive trials and several conclusions were arrived at. It was soon decided that the 'trackless' running feature was an unnecessary facility which would be rarely used and too complicated to worry about in combat conditions. Also the Christie hull was too narrow to take any existing British tank turret. However, the power-to-weight ratio was $2\frac{1}{2}$ times better than the best existing British tank.

It was therefore decided to retain the Christie suspension system and layout but build a new hull $5\frac{1}{2}$in wider and 10in longer to take the then standard 2pdr gun and turret. The American First World War vintage Liberty engine was retained and the Nuffield company, part of the Morris group, arranged to build it under licence.

The prototype of the revised design, the A13E2, was ready late in 1937 and was rigorously tested. It was found necessary to improve the clutch and transmission and govern the speed down to 30mph to conserve engine life. An order for 65 vehicles was placed at the beginning of 1938 and Nuffield completed these in the summer of 1939, less than 2½ years after the project was initiated. The A13 was also called the Cruiser Tank Mk III and these tanks were in service when the Second World War started.

A subsequent decision to increase hull, chassis, and turret armour led to the A13 Mk II (or Cruiser Tank Mk 4). This was literally the A13 with added armour. On the outbreak of war these Cruiser tanks represented the latest in British armour; over 600 were built and they saw service in the first two years or so of the Second World War. Future developments saw the continued application of the Christie design features to more sophisticated designs, dealt with in Chapter 8.

Meanwhile 'pirated' versions of the Christie BT type tank were in production in Poland and Czechoslovakia.

Christie's old enthusiasm was now greatly aroused. During the year that his M1932 was on trial in England, Christie had been hard at work in the USA producing a new, brilliant 1937 model for offer to the British, based on the interest which the British War Office had expressed. A brochure he produced at this time, titled 'Modern Mobile Defense', also outlined Christie's philosophy of armoured warfare – a philosophy which was the source of his inspiration. He wrote:

'My first object was to build a chassis that will protect the man who is to risk his life by facing the enemy and to provide a machine by the use of which he can defend himself and destroy the enemy. Therefore, we built a chassis with frontal lines and slopes that will make it almost impossible to penetrate the chassis with any type of projectile. Next, we constructed the chassis as low as possible, making it as inconspicuous as the power plant permits. We then turned to the next problem of defence which is speed. Speed in an aeroplane or speed on the ground is equally important. With speed you can surround the enemy, you can flank him, you can reach points quickly and take up positions to stop the advance. If you meet an overpowering force you can quickly evade it'.

These ideas were succinctly expressed, but Christie's brochure was not well received in England. The trials of the M1932 chassis, given the British designation A13E1, had long since been translated into a General Staff Requirement and from there, in the record time of 10 months, had been built into the prototype

cruiser tank A13E2 which, while using Christie's brilliant mechanical engineering principles, had considerably modified his concept of a fighting vehicle. An earlier British promise to purchase a new, later model was now quietly forgotten. Christie tried persistently for more than a month and, on February 20, 1938, wrote a long outline of his frustrations to the War Office ending with an offer to sell the new 1937 model and patent rights for $320000. By the end of March Christie was back in New York and, not for the first time in his life, practically penniless. He received a letter via his lawyers which abruptly summed up both his triumph and his brush-off: 'Dear Mr.Christie – You asked me for a confirmation of the speed which your experimental tank achieved under trial. On the flying quarter mile which is very slightly downhill it ran at 64·3mph. Yours sincerely, G. Le Q. Martel. Colonel, Deputy Director of Mechanization'.

This ended Christie's active participation in practical tank design, but his ideas lived on for years – in the Russian T-34 and the British Cromwell of the 1940s.

Top British-built A13E2 prototype based on the Christie M1932 prototype.

Above British A13, Cruiser Tank Mk III, was the production model, in service 1940–41.

A13 Mk II cruiser tanks
of 1940–41.

The T-34

The classic T-34 shape; a 1941 production model, typical of the earlier vehicles.

Arguably the Soviet Union's T-34 was the greatest tank design in the history of armoured vehicles, certainly it is generally held to have come the closest to the ideal. It balanced the qualities of fire power, armour protection and mobility as nearly to perfection as has yet been achieved. Coupled with this it enjoyed a high degree of reliability, was relatively simple to build and maintain, and was produced in large numbers; well over 40000 T-34 type vehicles are believed to have been built. The T-34 was so advanced for its time that it still proved quite

a viable fighting vehicle in the 1960s, thirty years after its battle debut. Into the 1970s large numbers of T-34s were still in service; although by then replaced in the armies of the main Soviet bloc states, the vehicle still served with the armies of many of the small nations within the Soviet sphere of influence.

The T-34 was derived directly from Christie's 'fast tank' concept of the 1930s and, with well judged development by the Soviet design teams, it provided a convincing vindication of his ideas.

Work which led to the T-34 started in 1934

T-34s were well suited to the climatic conditions of the East. The wide track shoes and low ground pressure gave them good speed in snow. These are 1943 production models pictured in February 1945; note the typical mix of all-steel and rubber-tyred wheels.

A T-34 crew cleaning the 76 mm gun. Note the standard padded helmet and dark blue coveralls. The vehicle is the 1940 production type with un-armoured hull machine gun.

when it was decided necessary to plan a successor for the Soviet medium tank of the period, the T-28. This vehicle was typical of 'conventional' 1930s tank design – a slow boxy, multi-turreted vehicle of which all the major powers had examples. Their appearance and characteristics were so similar as to suggest a good deal of stealing of ideas.

In 1934 the Christie type BT fast tank was being built and the chief engineer of the Kirov Works in Leningrad, Mikhail Koszkin, tried matching the Christie-type suspension to the

existing T-28 chassis. The resulting vehicle was known as the T-29-5. The best that could be said for it was that it was faster than its predecessor, but it offered no advance in fire power or shape.

Another design team at the Kharkov factory, under an engineer called Tsigankov, did the vital thinking that gave birth to the T-34. They reasoned that it was better to produce a heavier version of the BT than to try and adapt its characteristics to other designs. The latest BT tank at the time, the BT-7M, was taken and

1940 production models move forward to the battle front in September 1941. The squat shape with well-sloped armour is clearly shown.

Early production versions of the T34.

The classic Soviet armour/ infantry attack. Infantry squads ride forward on the vehicles which are provided with handrails for the purpose. These are 1942 models with all-steel wheels. The vehicles are in multi-colour camouflage, unusual on Russian tanks.

given a sloped armour hull in place of the original slab-sided structure. The resulting vehicle, the BT-IS (or 'Ispitatelinig') was promising, and in 1936 a special design team, headed by Koszkin and with A. Morozov as designer, was set up at Kharkov. Morozov had designed a fast medium tank, the T-46, which was not taken up. In 1937 an improved version of the BT-IS was built, the A-20 (later called the T-30). This retained the wheel or track running facility of the BT, and the BT's 45 mm gun, but it exhibited the now classic shape, with hull sides overhanging the tracks. Koszkin got permission to carry out further development and the result was the T-32, which dispensed at last with Christie's wheel or track options, and in which the 45 mm gun was replaced with a 76·2 mm short calibre weapon.

The T-32 was very successful on trials and a production order was contemplated. However, experience gained during the Spanish Civil War suggested the need for thicker armour. Suitable revision of the plans led to the T-33 and T-34. The former had the wheel and track option, the latter lacked it. The T-34 was accepted after very rigorous testing which included a trial march from Kharkov via Moscow, Smolensk, Kiev, and back to Kharkov.

Fortuitous war experience, in Finland and Manchuria, in 1939, led to various design conclusions which were all incorporated in T-34s. These included high-velocity guns and sloping armour (welded as opposed to rivetted). On the basis of the success achieved up to 1939 with electrically welded tank hulls and turrets, welded construction for further models was specified. Vulnerable to anti-tank guns, they had shown up badly during the Spanish Civil War. The following specifications were laid down for future designs:
1 New models should have a sloping armoured hull projecting over the tracks replacing the mudguards used hitherto, thus affording protection of this vulnerable spot from cannon fire.
2 All components must be of unit construction to facilitate repair by replacement of complete components.
3 All equipment in tank construction must be standardized and simplified.
4 Medium and heavy tanks must be fitted with wide tracks with small-pitched links and fully floating pins.
5 New models should have high top speed and good slope-climbing ability.
6 Hulls and turrets must be streamlined to prevent the lodgement of anti-tank projectiles.

7 The light and medium tanks must employ Christie type suspension, with singly suspended bogie wheels.

8 Future models are to utilize the newly-developed high-powered diesel engine and simple clutch and brake steering. This will increase the range of operations, reduce fire hazard and, at the same time, greatly simplify maintenance problems.

The T-34 reflected all these stipulations and an initial production order for 115 vehicles was placed, the Kirov Works at Stalingrad being the builders. The first two T-34s were kept somewhat fortuitously from premature revelation to the world by the termination of the Russo-Finnish war which ended in March 1940 just before the two prototypes arrived at the front for testing on active service. Thus they remained unknown to the Germans, who were to be ignorant of the new weapon until after their invasion of Russia in 1941.

The T-34 was noted for its excellently shaped hull and turret, made up of flat plates inclined at steep angles. This considerably increased its resistance to artillery rounds. The tank's armament, a 76·2mm gun of relatively long barrel length and high muzzle velocity, was new for tanks of this class. The use of a diesel engine reduced the risk of fire and greatly increased the radius of operation of the tank compared with tanks powered by petrol engines. The independent suspension permitted high speeds even on rough terrain whilst the wide tracks enhanced the ability to cross mud and snow and reduced the overall ground pressure. The design of the tank facilitated rapid mass-production as well as creating ideal conditions for the convenient execution of repairs in the field by one crew, or at most one repair unit.

The first T-34/76 was delivered to the Soviet Army in June 1940. The capacity of the tank industry was considerable but it was stipulated at the time that this new weapon be kept a closely-guarded secret. This held back mass production until the immediate threat of war. During the following year production of the T-34 was increased greatly, as it was now being shared by several other factories, and during the first six months a total of 1110 T-34s was produced.

When the Germans crossed the border in to Russia on June 22, 1941 production of T-34s had not been under way long enough to provide sufficient numbers for the Soviet Army. At this time at least half of the total Soviet tank strength (21000 tanks) was deployed in infantry-support

The Soviet-built T-54 tank was supplied to many countries friendly to Russia in the 1960s. *Above* An Egyptian T-54 burning after a direct hit from an Israeli Centurion tank during the October 1973 war. *Right* a T-54 of the Indian Army near Dacca during the 1967 Indo-Pakistan war, and *far right*, a Syrian T-54.

units, and BTs and T-26s comprised 75 per cent of the total tank strength.

Due to the speed of production it was not possible for some of the component plants to keep in step; a shortage of the new V-2 diesel engines led to some early T-34s being equipped with the older M-17 gasoline engine of the BT-7 and T-28 tanks. A hasty demand for a large number of transmissions also produced serious problems; the earlier units were so unreliable that some tanks went to battle with spare transmission assemblies secured to the engine compartment deck.

New tank plants were established at Kharkov, Mariupol, Kirov, Stalingrad, Voroshilovgrad, Nizhni-Tagil, Chelyabinsk, Chita and Novo-Sibirsk. Later, plants were set up at Saratov and Gorki. Apart from the tremendous losses of tanks in the 1941 campaigns, the Russians lost the Western industrial regions with their raw materials and skilled labour. The training of the crews was entirely inadequate, too – drivers and mechanics received only $1\frac{1}{2}$–2 hours' experience of tank driving before being seconded to operational units.

As the Germans penetrated further into Russia it became necessary to evacuate the majority of the tank plants as far as the Urals and Siberia. Subsequently, the T-34 was produced by a combine formed from the evacuated Kharkov factory (Komintern) and the original Nizhni-Tagil plant, established in the Urals and named the 'Ural Tank Building Establishment' (Uralmashzavod). Uralmashzavod produced T-34s under the direction of J.E.Maksarov, with A.Morozov as the Chief Engineer. The factory received the first blue-prints of the T-34 in July 1942 and the first production model from this plant was called 'Comrade Stalin'.

The T-34 came as a complete surprise to the Germans when it was first encountered in quantity in July 1941. Overnight it made all German designs then in service appear obsolete and under-gunned, for they were no match for the T-34 in either speed, hitting power or protection. This led immediately to the Germans speeding up Tiger tank output and to the design of the Panther which owed its appearance and features directly to the need to better the T-34.

Anatomy of the T-34

The T-34 was conventional in design, being made up of the following basic components: hull and turret, engine, transmission, steering unit, chassis and suspension, stowage and equipment. The most characteristic feature was the chassis. The suspension was of the Christie type, having five large double road wheels on each side, with a noticeably larger gap between the second and third wheels. The wheels were either cast or pressed. Each wheel was independently suspended, transversely swinging on a vertical coil spring, located on the inner side of the hull. The drive sprocket, located at the rear (to reduce vulnerability), was of the roller type used on the BT series, and drove a cast manganese steel track with centre guide-horns on alternate track blocks. An interesting feature was the method of retaining the track pins; welded to each side of the hull at the rear of the vehicle, level with the upper track, was a curved 'wiper' plate; the round-headed pins were inserted from the inner side of the track blocks, with no retention device at the outer end, and as the tracks rotated, these pins were pushed in. This method facilitated quick removal and replacement of track blocks. Track guards covered the entire top of the suspension system and extended 10in beyond the hull at the front and 4in at the rear.

The tank hull was made up of rolled armour plate, electro-welded throughout, although the upper rear plate and the engine cover plate were fastened by screws so they could be removed for access to the engine and transmission during inspection or repair. All plates were well-sloped to increase their immunity to armour-piercing rounds; with few exceptions only three different thicknesses of rolled armour plate were employed. The hull interior was divided into four sections: driving, fighting, engine and transmission.

Only one bulkhead was fitted within the vehicle, separating the fighting and engine compartments. The rear deck immediately behind the turret was slightly raised and accommodated a row of engine compartment grills and an engine access plate, with an exhaust pipe on each side. Hand rails on both sides of the hull were for use by tank-borne infantry.

In the driving compartment at the extreme front, there were two seats with inclined backs, intended for the driver/mechanic and the gunner/radio operator, together with the controls (main clutch pedal, foot-brake, fuel-injection pedal, two steering levers, brakes and gear-change lever), engine and instrument panels, a lever for opening and closing the shutters on the engine cover, two compressed air bottles and a control for varying the revs of the engine. Here also could be found some ammunition and on occasions radio equipment (originally only provided to platoon, company or higher commanders' tanks; in the T-34/85 tank the radio equipment was fitted in the turret). In the front left of the armoured hull top was the entrance hatch for the driver-mechanic; on his cover were mounted three observation periscopes (from Model 1942 onwards this entrance

A T-34 platoon carries infantry across a river in the Ukraine, 1944.

Re-loading a 1943 model T-34. This version had an enlarged octagonal turret.

Crews lined up to take over new vehicles provided by public donation. The vehicle on the extreme left is a KV-1, the remainder are T-34s.

Right Light tank M1A1—
this was Major General
Patton's command
vehicle, 2nd Armored
Division, during 1940.
Below left M3A1 of the US
Marine Corps, which saw
action at Guadalcanal in
1942.
Below right Light tank M3
(Stuart Mk 1) of the 8th
King's Royal Irish
Hussars, 4th Armoured
Brigade, in desert
camouflage, North
Africa 1941.

hatch was altered, equipped only with two episcopes in moveable armoured covers). On the right-hand side of the glacis plate was located the forward-firing DTM machine gun, with a horizontal fire arc of 24 degrees, and a vertical arc of $-6/+12$ degrees (from Model 1942 onwards additional armoured covers were provided over this machine-gun mounting). In a foot position at the bottom of the hull was located a pedal (sometimes referred to as 'Desantov') which enabled the driver to render the tank immobile, even under enemy fire. The driver/ mechanic compartment was not separated from the fighting compartment by bulkheads, and hence was accessible with the turret at any position.

The fighting compartment was located in the middle of the hull. On the floor and walls were the main ammunition bins; a proportion of the ammunition was placed in special containers, the remainder in boxes. On the sides of the hull were also the fuel tanks as well as elements of the suspension. The steering and transmission shafts passed under the floor.

The fighting compartment was enclosed by the turret, which rested in a bed. The turret in all models was very low, primarily to reduce the overall height of the tank. This feature restricted the depression of the main and auxilliary armament – especially when firing on a reverse slope or at ground troops on foot at close ranges. In the turret, which had no basket, was located the main armament – a 76·2mm gun – coaxially mounted with a DT (or DTM) machine gun, sighting and observation devices and some of the ammunition for the main armament and machine gun. There were also seats for the crew, the commander (who also functioned as gun layer) and loader. The turret was traversed with the aid of a special traversing mechanism driven by an electric motor; it also had a special lock preventing unnecessary freedom of rotation. The gun was elevated with the aid of a hand wheel operated by the gun layer.

A bulkhead seperated the fighting compartment from the engine compartment. Here was mounted the V-2 12-cylinder water-cooled diesel, producing 490bhp at 1800rpm, together with fuel injection, cooling, lubrication and ignition systems and four batteries.

The transmission compartment housed the main clutch, ventilators, gearbox, final drives, brakes, electric starter, transfer box and the two main fuel tanks. Auxiliary tanks could be carried – four cylindrical tanks on the sides and two smaller cylindrical ones on the rear hull plate. The transmission system was found to be generally troublesome. The T-34 was steered by the clutch and brake method and controlled by steering levers; there was no power-assisted control gear used on this tank.

All the T-34/76 models were armed with a semi-automatic 76·2mm gun with self-locking breech block.

Following the Soviet practice of a high degree of standardization, the T-34, and its companion vehicle the early KV tank, had a great number of interchangeable parts; engine, armament, transmission, periscopes, etc. In its design the Russians had aimed at mechanical simplicity. All models had the same hull and suspension components, although there were differences in the type of track and bogie wheels employed. Some tanks were fitted with steel-tyred wheels due to a shortage of rubber at an early stage in the war; these wheels had internal shock-absorbers to reduce wear. When rubber once more became available in 1943, production of rubber-tyred bogie wheels was resumed.

The T-34 Model 1940 had a long engine deck and a welded turret with distinctive overhang. The turret hatch was clumsy – occupying the entire rear part of the turret, making it heavy to lift and also blocking the commander's view when open. Only one periscope was fitted on the turret – at the front on the left-hand side. The tank had a flat, linked plate track.

The second model of the T-34 tank appeared in 1941, and had a rolled plate turret with a more powerful Model 1940 (F-34) 76·2mm L/41·5 gun. The F-34 Model 40 gun was greatly improved and had a barrel length of 41·5 calibres. At first the gun fired an anti-tank round weighing 13·9lb with a muzzle-velocity of 2000fps, and at ranges of 500, 1000, 1500 and 2000 metres, penetrations of 69, 61, 54 and 48mm could be achieved. During 1943 a sub-calibre (arrowhead) round was introduced, weighing 6·7lbs and having a muzzle velocity of 2950fps. At ranges of 500 and 1000 metres it could achieve armour penetrations of 92 and 58mm respectively.

The 76·2mm gun could be fired by either of two methods, by hand or by foot pedal. The 7·62mm DTMG (or its later version, the DTM), mounted both coaxially with the main armament and in the hull front, was a model derived from the well-known DTMG designed by Degtarov specifically for tank use; it could fire at the rate of 600rpm and each magazine held 60–63 rounds.

There were very many detail variations and changes in the T-34 during its production run. The most important features were unchanged even though there were structural alterations. For example, the Model 1942 featured a new cast turret, and a greatly modernized vehicle, the T-34M, appeared. As originally designed the T-34M retained the features of the Model 42 but had torsion bar suspension with small wheels

64

as on KV heavy tanks. However, as this would have caused much disruption in changing the production lines, the Christie suspension was retained. A new hexagonal turret, designed by Morozov, was produced specifically to eliminate a shell trap which was discovered under the rear overhang of the early type turrets. The Model 43 was a further improved type, with cupola for commander and a five-speed gearbox replacing the original four-speed type. Stronger track and cast wheels were other changes.

The T-34/85

The necessity to provide a proven gun, of long range, firing a round able to pierce the armour of the new German tanks at greater ranges than that of the 76·2mm gun, became the requisite for both medium and heavy tanks. A rapid means of providing the Red Army with a medium tank having more powerful armament was by modernizing the T-34 to mount a modified form of the 85mm AA gun Model 1939, and this was accomplished towards the end of 1943. During Autumn 1943 a prototype was built of an up-gunned T-34 tank. The new tank designed by Morozov and V.V.Krylov was designated the T-34/85. It utilized a modified form of turret originally designed for the KV-85 heavy tank with a ring diameter of 5·2ft and which accommodated an extra crew member, thus easing the work-load of the gunner and commander. Designed during the Summer of 1943 the tank was approved for mass production on December 15, 1943, and by the end of the year 283 had been produced. During the following year about 11000 tanks of this type were manufactured. It was originally issued to élite guards armoured brigades during the Spring of 1944, but when production reached a reasonable

level it became the standard medium tank in all armoured units. Also used on the initial series of tanks was the semi-automatic 85mm gun designed by General F.F.Petrov, designated D-5T. Later models received a further version, the ZIS S-53 (M-1943) L/51·5 gun, designed by General Grabin. Both weapons had almost identical ballistic properties and at a range of 1000 metres was claimed by the Russians to have been able to penetrate the 100mm frontal armour of the German Tiger tank, as well as that of the Panther.

Besides its more powerful armament, the T-34/85 had thicker turret armour. The slight increase in the turret weight, however, did not greatly decrease its mobility, nor its cross-country performance. On the other hand, the large calibre armament with greater ballistic range provided combat parity with enemy heavy tanks.

In 1947 an improved model of the T-34/85 tank was introduced. This was basically the same tank with improvements in transmission, armour arrangement, and more sophisticated fire-control and vision devices. It was used extensively during the Korean War. During the 1950s production of the T-34/85 continued under licence in Poland and Czechoslovakia, where it was extensively modified. Production of the T-34 ceased in June 1964, by which time some 12000 had been produced with the 85mm gun. In 1939–40, 115 T-34s were completed, and production built up to 2810 in 1941, 5015 in 1942, 10000 in 1943, and 11758 in 1944; during the last phase, 1947–64, 12000 were built.

Specialized Variants

There were several special purpose conversions of the basic T-34 design. Extensive use was made of turretless T-34s for recovery purposes. The weights of these vehicles varied, but generally they were in the region of 30 tons. Such ARVs were collectively called TT-34. The first specialized recovery vehicle was the SKP-5 which consisted of a T-34 chassis with a special 360 degree traverse crane of five ton capacity.

Above left T-34s and infantry in an attack. The nearest vehicle has all-steel wheels on its three centre axles, and stowage boxes at the rear.

Above right T-34s move at speed towards the front, in Hungary.

Yugoslav-built T-34/85 85mm

T-34-T: During the early 1950s the Russians fitted T-34 recovery vehicles with specialized equipment such as dismountable cranes, boxes for spare parts and winches, and some with pushing bars. This type was called the T-34-T. Changes included the addition of a radio set, a rigging assembly, a loading platform and a jib crane. The rear deck of the vehicle had a cargo platform of 2½ tons capacity, designed for carrying equipment and tank accessories.

There were two T-34 MTV versions in the bridge-laying configuration, both produced after the end of the Second World War. The first was an early type with a rigid ARK type bridge, the second a model with a rigid type bridge launched by pivoting about a roller at the front (designated T-34 MTU).

Flame Throwers With the standardization of the T-34 and KV programmes, flame-thrower installations were designed for both tanks; the T-34 was originally tried out with a type designated ATO-41. Further flame thrower development was influenced by the policy of the US and British armies. The former preferred the replacement of the main armament by the flame gun, and the latter insisted upon the retention of the main armament at all cost; of the two, the Russians preferred the British method, although they were against the employment of towed fuel trailers. In 1943, under the Allied Aid Agreement, a unit of British flame-throwing tanks (Churchill Crocodiles) were shipped to Russia for training purposes. As the result of the experience gained from the flame installation in the Churchill tank, the T-34 system was completely redesigned, and the flame thrower redesignated ATO-42. Tanks so equipped became known as OT-34 (Ogniemetnyi Tank 34), and were first employed against the Germans in 1944.

While the T-34 itself soldiered on into the 1970s, in all its various forms and under many flags, the Soviet Union continued the breed in a succession of designs which each represented a logical improvement on its predecessor and provided a direct line of development from the T-34.

The T-44 was a 1944 design which saw limited service in the early post-war years. It was essentially an improved T-34/85. Flat instead of sloped hull sides allowed space for a larger turret, and the hull was longer and lower. This vehicle was very much an interim design and

only a few were made. It seems possible that it was unsatisfactory and it may well have been that the weight was too much for the Christie suspension – certainly this problem was encountered by the British when developing ever larger cruiser tank designs in the 1940s.

At all events, in the T-54 which appeared in 1947 as a successor to the T-34 and T-44, the Christie suspension was abandoned in favour of the simpler and sturdier torsion bar suspension.

The T-54 was an excellent design which remained first-line equipment right into the 1970s with Soviet bloc nations. Of similar size to the T-34, the T-54 was lower and, if anything, more compact. The main armament, a 100mm gun, was improved in successive marks, and later vehicles had comprehensive infra-red night-fighting sights linked to the guns. When this was introduced in 1958 the T-54 was the first tank with IR equipment as standard.

Compared to the T-34, the T-54 has a simpler hull with vertical sides and a sloped glacis. The V-54G V12 diesel engine of the T-54 is simply a slightly refined version of the old V-2 engine of the T-34, but it is mounted traversely, thus saving valuable space. All the well-proven features of the T-34 were retained in the T-54, right down to the simple but clever method of retaining the dry pins on the track shoes by striking them on a cam on the final drive housing – an automatic process preventing the pins working loose.

The T-54 turret is the ballistically superb 'inverted frying pan' which originated with the Josef Stalin 3 heavy tank. Essentially the turret is very simple and functional. The gun trunnions are set well back and a splash plate around the gun inside the turret replaces the more conventional mantlet. A gyro-stabilizer for the gun was a major innovation in the T-54, bringing it into line with Western tanks in the matter of refined fire control. There have been many marks of T-54, some later models also being called T-55. China made a licence-built version, the T-49. Variants have included mine-clearers, recovery vehicles and bridgelayers.

The T-62, which first appeared in 1961, is virtually a slightly lengthened version of T-54, with a 115mm gun of smooth bore, firing fin-stabilized ammunition. In all other essentials, however, it is similar to the T-54. In the 1970s a further refinement of the design appeared, the T-70, longer yet and with the turret set slightly further back.

In all the Soviet Union's medium tank line displays a remarkable pedigree – over 40 years of consistent and careful development from the BT of the early 1930s to the T-34s, T-54s, T-62s and others which were all in service in the 1970s.

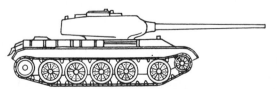

T-44 85 mm

The American Light Tanks

While the cheap and simple light tanks and tankettes produced in Europe did not stand the test of war – and rapidly disappeared from combat use after their vulnerability was demonstrated – the American light tanks which originated in the 1930s played a big part in the fortunes of the Allied armies in the Second World War. There is no anomaly in this statement for the American 'light' tanks were nearly as big and harder hitting than the British cruiser tanks they replaced, and could not be compared size for size with British, Italian and German light tanks. Aside, perhaps, from the Chaffee of 1945, which was a far cry from anyone's conception of a 'light' tank, there was no really outstanding individual light tank model. But the light tank family conceived in America had the right balance of fire power, mobility, technical excellence, and simplicity to suit the weapon to the conditions of the time, and as such the story of their development is of interest.

Following the general run-down of American forces at the end of the First World War, the American General Staff disbanded the Tank Corps in 1919 and under the National Defense Act of 1920, tanks and tank development (in conjunction with the Ordnance Department) became an infantry responsibility. The General Staff subsequently defined the role of the tank in future war 'to facilitate the uninterrupted advance of the rifleman in the attack'. For economic and operational reasons, future tanks were to be concentrated on 'light' and 'medium' types, the former restricted to 5 tons in weight so as to be transportable by truck, and the latter limited to 15 tons to meet military bridging restrictions.

As already recounted, J. Walter Christie wooed the Ordnance Board with his own fast light tank designs, but aside from a token handful of vehicles his projects were spurned and the Ordnance Department produced their own concept of what was required. Severe financial limitations throughout the 1920s allowed the production of only about two experimental tanks a year, culminating in the T1E4 light tank of 1931 which established the layout of rear engine and front sprocket drive adopted in all subsequent US light tanks.

In 1927 the American General Staff had set up a very small Experimental Mechanized Force, largely influenced by the similar unit which the British had just established, drawn mainly from infantry tank units and with the emphasis on light tanks. By 1931, however, General Douglas MacArthur decided that in the mechanized age the US Cavalry, equipped with tanks and armoured cars, had an 'exploiting' role in armoured warfare quite distinct from the infantry support role envisaged for tanks in the US Army until that time. The cavalry took over the Mechanized Force and was authorized to equip itself with tanks. To conform with the 1920 Defense Act cavalry tanks were known as 'combat cars', a legal formality necessary to overcome the rule making tanks a prerogative of the infantry.

By 1934–35, further experimental light tanks had been produced, T2, T2E1 and T2E2. The T2 itself had features inspired by the Vickers Armstrong 6 ton tank including the Vickers type leaf spring suspension. For economy reasons, it was desirable that the light 'combat cars' for the cavalry should be adapted from the infantry's light tanks. Concurrent with the T2 light tank, therefore, Rock Island Arsenal pro-

Honeys in the Western Desert. Stuart Mk I light tanks (M3 Light) on exercises soon after delivery to British troops in 1941.

duced a similar vehicle for cavalry use, the T5 combat car. This differed from the T2 principally in having vertical volute spring suspension instead of leaf spring suspension. Development led to the T5E2 and, under the designation M1 Combat Car, this vehicle entered service with the US Cavalry in 1937. Armament of the M1 was a ·30 and ·50 calibre machine gun in the turret and another ·30 calibre weapon in the hull front. Engine was a 7 cylinder Continental gasoline type which gave a top speed of 45 mph, the crew was four men and weight was 9·7 (short) tons. An improved model, the M2 Combat Car, had a trailing idler to give a lengthened ground contact and improved ride.

In July, 1940, the new Armored Force was created, abolishing the division between infantry and cavalry tank units. The 'combat car' term was now no longer necessary and the M1 and M2 Combat Cars were then redesignated Light Tank M1A1 and M1A2. These vehicles did not see combat in the Second World War, but some were used for training at Fort Knox and other centres. The M1/M2 Combat Car series was, however, important as the basis for most subsequent US light tank designs until 1944, and much useful operating and design experience was gained with these early models.

The T2 light tank, meanwhile, had been designed and built at Rock Island Arsenal and was produced in 1933. It had a simple riveted box-like hull with rear-mounted engine and drive to the front sprockets. These features were inherited from the later T1 series experimental tanks but the suspension was copied from the Vickers 6 ton light tank (see Chapter 3)

which had been demonstrated in America. Comparative trials with the contemporary T5 Combat Car showed, however, that the vertical volute suspension of this vehicle was much superior to the Vickers leaf spring suspension, and it was fitted in a second light tank prototype, T2E1, produced after the trials in April 1934. For the infantry support role for which all American tanks were envisaged in the mid 1930s, a machine gun armament was considered sufficient, and in the T2E1 this consisted of a ·30 calibre and a ·50 calibre Browning mounted in a single turret which stretched nearly the whole width of the hull. A second ·30 calibre machine gun was mounted in the hull front. The T2E1 was standardized late in 1935 and put into production at Rock Island Arsenal under the designation Light Tank M2A1, 19 vehicles being built in addition to the pilot model.

Meanwhile an improved vehicle, the T2E2 was built which was identical to the T2E1 save that it had two turrets side by side, one for each machine gun, instead of the single full-width

superstructure. This was standardized and put into production in 1936–37 as the Light Tank M2A2.

In 1938 improvements were incorporated in production vehicles to give better riding qualities. These included longer stroke springs in the bogies with the rear bogies set 11 in further back. The improved model was designated Light Tank M2A3.

Light Tanks M2A1, M2A2, and M2A3 were all considered obsolete by 1940 and none was used in combat, although they did perform a useful training role in the early war years. Final versions of this type in production were the M2A2E3 and M2A3E3, which were re-engined with diesel power units.

Final and most important vehicle in the M2 light tank series was the M2A4. Comparative experience with the M2 light tanks and the corresponding M1 combat cars showed the advantages of the single turret in the latter. In 1939 Rock Island Arsenal designed an improved version of the M2A3 reflecting user experience.

Opposite top Light Tank T1E4 was one of the prototype series from which the American light tanks were developed. Note the similarity of layout and suspension to Vickers 6 tonner.
Opposite centre Light Tank M2A3 at speed during 1940 'war games'. This model did not see war service.
Opposite bottom Light Tanks M2A2 exercise in tackling tree stump obstacles at Fort Benning, Georgia, March 1940. They were simulating tactics observed in the 1939 Polish campaign.
Above Light Tank M2A4 of the US Marine Corps at Guadalcanal, Solomon Islands, September 1942. Note the cupola and vision ports.

69

Standard production M3 light tank, showing riveted construction, cupola, and trailing idler. Sponson machine guns have been removed.

Light Tank M3A1 had a riveted hull and cast and welded turret with no cupola. Later, the hull was welded too.

Designated M2A4, this was basically the M2A3 with a traversing turret replacing the twin turrets, a 37mm gun as main armament, three hull machine guns, and thicker armour with 25mm maximum.

In September 1939 war was declared in Europe, giving added urgency to the American re-armament programme. Rock Island Arsenal, which had been responsible for the limited peace-time production of the US Army tanks, guns, and munitions, lacked space and facilities for tank production on the huge scale now envisaged for future American tank requirements. The Ordnance Department had planned to contract with commercial heavy engineering firms if extensive tank production was required in emergency, and tenders were thus invited for building the new M2A4. The contract, initially for 329 vehicles, went to American Car and Foundry in October 1939 and the first

production vehicle was delivered in April 1940. Meanwhile the order was increased to 365 vehicles and the final production M2A4 was eventually delivered in March 1941. The M2A4 was used in the early Pacific campaigns, but most were used for training. Some were supplied to Britain and Canada for training purposes too.

The Light Tank M3 was a progressive improvement on the M2A4, designed early in 1940, and incorporating lessons observed from the tank fighting in Europe in the 1939–40 campaigns. The main requirement was for increased armour thickness, and this in turn called for stronger suspension. Maximum frontal armour was increased to 38mm (51mm on the nose) and the vision ports in the turret sides were eliminated. A large trailing idler was fitted to increase ground contact. Other modifications included a lengthened rear superstructure and improved armour on the engine covers as a precaution against strafing from the air. The M3 was approved and standardized in July 1940 and entered production in March 1941 at American Car and Foundry, being introduced straight on to the line after completion of the M2A4 contract. This was the start of the 'flow line' techniques, adopted from automobile industry methods, which enabled America to supply the Allies with a never ending supply of armaments, turned out at a prodigous rate.

Several further improvements were made during production, first of these being a welded turret, replacing the riveted type, which was developed in late 1940 and introduced almost immediately into production vehicles in March 1941. This change was mainly to reduce weight, though it also eliminated the danger of 'popping' rivets in event of a hit. A further change was introduced in early 1941 with a welded/cast homogenous turret of rounded shape replacing the multi-faced turret used until then. This was later incorporated into production vehicles. From mid 1941 a gyro-stabilizer was fitted for the gun and in the fall of 1941, following British experience with M3 light tanks in the North African desert fighting, two 25 gallon jettisonable fuel tanks were added to increase the range. From early 1942 an all-welded hull was adopted. To ease engine supply problems, 500 M3 light tanks were completed with Guiberson T1020 diesel engines replacing the standard Continental petrol engine. These vehicles were sometimes called M3 (Diesel). Externally they were identical to the standard M3.

A further improved model was designed, tested, approved and standardized in August 1941. This had the cupola eliminated to reduce overall height, a gyro-stabilizer for the gun, power traverse for the turret, and a turret basket. Designated M3A1 it was introduced to the American Car and Foundry production line in June 1942 to follow the M3, which finally went

Last of the M3 light series was the M3A3 (British Stuart Mk V) with re-shaped all-welded hull, side skirts, welded turret, and thicker armour (*above*). Compare its shape with its production successor, the M5 (*below*), which had a larger turret and raised rear deck to clear the larger engine. The vehicle shown is for 'psychwar' service, and has a high-power loudspeaker to address enemy troops.

Light Tank M5 (British Stuart VI) demonstrates its agility in this, its first officially issued photograph.

out of production in August 1942.

A further change in the M3A1 was the elimination of the two sponson machine guns carried in the M2A4 and M3. These were fired remotely by the driver and proved of limited value, being finally sacrificed to reduce weight, and increase interior stowage. The British had already removed these guns from many of the M3s delivered to them.

Final production variant was the M3A3 which represented a radical redesign with a new all-welded hull enlarged by extending the sponsons and the driver's compartment forward and upward. This gave room for extra fuel tanks and increased ammunition stowage. Sandshields (another lesson from the desert fighting), were added and numerous other detail changes were made. Standardized in August 1942, the M3A3 entered production in early 1943.

There were many variants based on the M3 chassis, including gun towers, command vehicles, and mine clearers, mine exploders, and flame throwers. These M3 models saw wide service with British and Commonwealth forces, especially in the Western Desert in 1942. In British service the M3 was known as the 'Honey', unofficially, but was officially called General Stuart or Stuart.

The M3's successor, the Tank M5, originated in a suggestion by Cadillac division of GMC to the Ordnance Department that they should try the M3 light tank with twin Cadillac engines installed and the commercial Cadillac Hydramatic transmission which was produced for cars. In late 1941, a standard M3 was converted as a trials vehicle (the M3E2) to test the idea, and it proved most successful. This made a trouble-free 500 mile trial run, and the Cadillac-powered vehicle proved easy to drive, and smooth to operate. Due to the always acute shortage of Continental engines, the Cadillac modified vehicle was approved for production and standardized as the Light Tank M5 in February 1942. It was originally to be designated Light Tank M4, but this was changed to M5 to avoid confusion with the M4 medium tank (Sherman), then going into production.

To accommodate the twin Cadillac engines, the rear engine covers were stepped up. But the hull was otherwise similar in shape to that of the welded M3A1 apart from a sloping glacis. Turret installation, with basket and gyro-stabilizer, was tested in another development vehicle, M3E3, while in the following July another Cadillac facility, at Southgate, California, also commenced production. At the same time Massey-Harris commenced M5 production in Racine, Wisconsin, under the 'parentage' of Cadillac, and finally, in October 1943, when M3 series production ceased, American Car and

Foundry also switched to turning out M5s.

The M5A1 was designed and standardized in September 1942 to bring the M5 up to the standard of the much-improved M3A3. Among changes common with the M3A3 were a new turret with bulge at the rear for a radio installation, larger access hatches for the driver and co-driver, improved mount for the 37mm gun, and improved vision devices. In addition there was better water sealing on the hatches, an escape hatch added in the hull floor, and dual traverse allowing the commander to train the turret while firing his AA machine gun. There were also detachable sand shields. A later modification was the provision of a detachable shield/fairing on the turret side to protect the AA machine gun mount. From early 1943, the M5A1 replaced the M5 on production lines.

An important variant was the M8 Howitzer Motor Carriage which had a 75mm howitzer in an open-topped turret replacing the normal turret. This vehicle equipped the HQ companies of medium tank battalions in 1944–45 to give support fire.

Reports of the British experiences in the Western Desert fighting in 1942, when the 8th Army was using M3 series light tanks, showed that a heavier weapon was desirable for future US light tanks. A 75mm gun was fitted experimentally to a M8 Howitzer Motor Carriage in place of the howitzer, and trials proved that it would be possible to develop a version of the M5 series light tank armed with the 75mm gun. Stowage space was severely restricted in the M5, however, more so with the fitting of a 75mm gun, and in addition the overall design of this vehicle was now dated and the armour thickness was inadequate. In April 1943, therefore, the Ordnance Department, in conjunction with Cadillac (makers of the M5 series), began work on an entirely new light tank design which was to incorporate the best combinations of features from earlier designs with all lessons learned from previous experience. The twin Cadillac engines and Hydra-matic transmission which had been so successful and trouble-free in the M5 series were retained and the good accessibility which had been a feature of the T7 layout was adopted. A weight of 18 tons was envisaged with an armour basis of only 25mm to save

M3A3 'Stuart' 37mm

Culmination of American light tank development in the Second World War was the M24 Chaffee, in service by late 1944. This vehicle of the 7th Army speeds through Dambach during the advance into Germany.

73

Right Twin 40mm AA guns on the Chaffee hull produced the widely used M19 AA Gun Motor Carriage in 1945, still serving some armies 30 years later for battlefield AA protection. M42A1 (*lower*) is a similar derivative of the M41 Walker Bulldog tank which was an improved Chaffee. This vehicle is in Vietnam in 1969.

Below M24 Chaffee demonstrates its good flotation over soft going as it races full speed for cover during the 'Battle of the Bulge', December 1944.

weight, but with all hull faces angled for optimum protection. Maximum turret armour was 37mm. Vertical volute suspension was replaced by road wheels on torsion arms to give a smoother ride. First of two pilot models, designated T24, was delivered in October 1943 and proved so successful that the Ordnance Department immediately authorized a production order for 1000 vehicles, which was later raised to 5000. Cadillac and Massey-Harris undertook production, commencing March 1944, and these two plants between them produced 4415 vehicles (included SP variants) by the war's end. In each case production supplanted M5 series vehicles.

The 75mm M6 gun was adapted from the heavy aircraft cannon used in the Mitchell bomber, and had a concentric recoil system which saved valuable turret space. The T24 was standardized as the Light Tank M24 in May 1944. First deliveries of M24s were made to American tank battalions in late 1944, supplanting M5s, and the M24 came into increasing use in the closing months of the war, remaining as standard American light tank for many years afterwards, and being widely used in the Korean War. A 1950s development from this design was the Walker Bulldog, M41, an equally successful (and very similar) design with 76·2mm gun and larger turret.

Parallel to the need for a new light tank was the desire to produce a standard chassis as the basis of the so-called 'Light Combat Team' – a complete series of tanks, SP guns, and special purpose tanks all based on one chassis, so greatly simplifying maintenance and production. Each had identical engine, power train, and suspension to the M24. Among these were the M19 Gun Motor Carriage (an AA tank), M37 Howitzer Motor Carriage (105mm), and M41 Howitzer Motor Carriage (155mm). The Second World War was over before this standardization programme was completed.

All American light tanks built in the war years were supplied to other Allied nations. Major users were Canada, Britain, France, Japan (post-war), and Italy (post-war). The Chaffee, in particular, remains a fine example of technical achievement, packing a powerful punch into a compact layout. Both the Chaffee and Walker Bulldog served well into the 1970s, particularly with NATO forces and others (for example Japanese Self-Defense Force) within the American sphere of influence.

The awesome PzKpfw VI Ausf E Tiger as it first appeared on the Russian Front in 1942.

The story of the Tiger Tanks started in 1937, well before the outbreak of war. In 1939 the big engineering firm of Henschel u. Sohn GmbH of Kassel was instructed to design and construct a 30–33 ton tank intended to replace the early Panzer IV tanks, the vehicle being known as the DW.1 (DW was an abbreviation of Durchbruchswagen or 'breakthrough vehicle'). This early design featured a chassis with interleaved road wheels and the first vehicle was ready in September 1938. However, just after testing had commenced, the trials were suspended to allow work to be carried out on a new design for a requirement for a massive 65 ton tank, the VK.6501.[1]

Two prototypes of the VK.6501 were built and were undergoing trials when this project in turn was cancelled and development of the DW.1 resumed. By 1940, Henschel had so improved the original design that it was renamed DW.2; in this form it weighed 32 tons and had a crew of five. The planned armament was the short 7·5 cm gun, as on the PzKpfw IV, with two MG 34 machine guns. Trials were carried out with a prototype chassis until 1941, by which time Henschel had received an order for a new design in the same class and weight as the DW.2. The development code for the new vehicle was VK.3001. This order was also given to Henschel's competitors, Porsche, MAN, and Daimler-Benz. The Henschel version, VK.3001(H), was a development of the DW.2. Four prototypes were built, differing only in detail from one another, two in March 1941 and two the following October. The superstructure of the VK.3001(H) resembled the PzKpfw IV, and the suspension consisted of seven interleaved road wheels and three return rollers per side. It was planned to mount the 7·5 cm L/48 gun in this vehicle, but due to the appearance of the Russian T-34 with its 76mm gun, it became obsolete and development was discontinued. Two of the VK.3001(H) chassis were, however, converted to self-propelled guns by lengthening and fitting a lightly armoured superstructure, and mounting a 12·8 cm K.40 gun. These two vehicles were used in Russia in 1942.

The Soviet T-34 was to have a profound effect on all new German tank design. The Panther tank (page 88) was a fresh design in 1942 which was directly influenced by the T-34 and copied many of its features. The VK.3001 and its immediate derivations, however, were already designed when the T-34 was first encountered, so did not embody any lessons from this Russian vehicle.

Concurrently with the order for the VK.3001 an additional order had also been placed in 1941 for a 36 ton tank designated VK.3601. The specification for this design had been proposed by Hitler; it included a powerful high velocity gun, heavy armour, and a maximum speed of at least 40kmh. A prototype of this project was built by Henschel in March 1942, but experimental work on both the VK.3001 and VK.3601 was stopped when a further order for a 45 ton tank was received in May 1941. Designated VK.4501, it was proposed that the vehicle would mount a tank version of the 8·8 cm anti-aircraft gun. With the order came a stipulation that the prototype was to be ready in time for Hitler's birthday on April 20, 1942, when a full demonstration of its capabilities was to be staged. As design time was limited, Henschel

76

[1] Vollkettenkraftfahrzeug – meaning 'fully tracked experimental vehicle, 65 tons, first design'. Also known as the SW (Sturmwagen 'assault vehicle') or PzKpfw VII.

The German Heavy Tanks

Porsche had also received the order for the Vk.4501 and like Henschel they decided to use the experience and features from their previous model the VK.3001(P), which had performed well on trials.

The demonstration of the two competing prototypes, the VK.4501(H) and VK.4501(P) type 101, took place before Hitler at Rastenburg on April 20. The Henschel design was judged to be superior, being very conventional in layout and construction despite its large size. An order for production to commence in August 1942 was given and the vehicle was designated Panzerkampfwagen VI Tiger Ausf.H; the Sonderkraftfahrzeug, or Ordnance Number was SdKfz 181. In February 1944 the designation was changed to PzKpfw Tiger Ausf.E, SdKfz 181.

The Tiger was in production for two years, from August 1942 until August 1944, and in this period some 1350 vehicles were delivered out of 1376 ordered. Maximum monthly production was achieved in April 1944, when 104 Tigers were built. The specified weight of 45 tons was exceeded in production models by as much as 11 tons.

At the time of its first appearance in service in late 1942, the PzKpfw VI Tiger I Ausf.H was an outstanding design with its 8·8cm gun and armour protection up to 100mm thick. These features made the 45 ton Tiger the most formidable fighting vehicle then in service. Tiger I was the first German combat tank to be fitted with overlapping road wheel suspension, arranged with triple overlapping and interleaved wheels of a steel disc type with solid rubber tyres. In later vehicles these discs were steel-tyred and internally sprung, an idea taken from Russian practice. The overlapping wheel system

decided to incorporate the best features of their VK.3001(H) and VK.3601(H) projects into a vehicle of the weight and class required. Henschel were to build two models, the type H1 mounting an 8·8cm 36 L/56 and the type H2 a 7·5 cm KwK L/70, in a Porsche turret, although the H2 existed only as a wooden mock up at that time.

The Porsche version of the VK.3001 was also known to its designers as the Leopard or Typ 100. This turretless prototype incorporated several new design features such as petrol-electric drive and longitudinal torsion bar suspension. MAN and Daimler-Benz also constructed prototypes to this design but like the Henschel project they had become obsolete.

An early production Tiger fully stowed and fitted with equipment, including smoke dischargers and Feifel air filter apparatus (on the rear deck) for tropical service.

was adopted for optimum weight distribution. There were eight independently sprung torsion bar axles on each side. In order to carry all the axles inside the hull envelope it was necessary to stagger them on the floor so that the right hand axles trailed aft and the left hand axles led forward. It was thus possible to incorporate the maximum number within the vehicle's length, and this resulted in an extremely soft and stable ride for a tank of this weight and size. Two types of track were used; a wide type measuring 28½in was fitted for combat and narrow type, 20½in wide, for travel and transportation. When the narrow tracks were fitted the outer wheels were removed from each suspension unit. This type of suspension gave a superior ride, but it also had its drawbacks, one being that the interleaved wheels were liable to become packed with mud and snow during winter fighting and if ignored until frozen this could jam the wheels. The Russians discovered this and took advantage of the situation by timing their attacks for dawn when the German vehicles were likely to have become immobilized by freezing snow or mud during the overnight lay-up.

The Tiger was originally fitted with a Maybach V-12 petrol engine, the 21 litre HL 210 P45, but it was soon realized that the vehicle was underpowered and, from December 1943, the 24 litre HL 230 P45 was substituted. The Tigers used in North Africa and Southern Russia were fitted with an air cleaner system called Feifel. This was attached to the rear of the hull and linked to the engine by means of the engine cover plate. These tropical Tigers were known as the Tiger (Tp). The Feifel air system was discontinued as an economy measure on vehicles built in early 1943. While all earlier designs of German tank had the simple clutch-and-brake type of steering, the Tiger's greatly increased weight necessitated a more refined system. Henschel therefore developed and adopted a special steering unit, similar to the British Merritt-Brown type, which was fully regenerative and continuous. It had the added feature of a twin radius of turn in each gear. The gearbox, which was based on earlier Maybach types, gave no less than eight forward gear ratios and, with its pre-selector, made the Tiger very light and easy to handle for a vehicle of its size.

The Tiger's mechanical layout followed that of previous operational German designs in that the transmission shaft led forward beneath the turret cage to the gearbox set alongside the driver. The steering unit was mounted transversely in the nose of the tank, a bevel drive leading to a final reduction gear in each front sprocket. Power take-off for the hydraulic turret traverse unit, mounted in the turret floor, was taken from the rear of the gearbox, and it is typical of the Tiger's well thought out design that the hydraulic unit could be disconnected from the power drive shaft by releasing a dog-clutch, thus allowing the turret to be lifted from the vehicle without the complications of disconnecting any other joints or pipes.

Because the Tiger's 56 ton weight was too much for most bridges, arrangements for wading and total submersion to a depth of 13ft with Snorkel breathing were introduced on the first 495 Tigers produced, and then abandoned on all subsequent vehicles (for economy reasons) leaving them capable of wading only to a depth of about 4ft. The method used for total submersion of the first 495 vehicles was very ingenious. All hatches and doors were rubber sealed and the turret ring was sealed by means of an inflatable rubber tube. The gun mantlet was sealed by a sliding frame, with a rubber sealing ring, and the machine-gun ports were provided with expanding rubber plugs which were inserted when the machine-guns were dismounted. The main air supply for the crew and engine was obtained through a three-piece Snorkel pipe that was mounted on the engine compartment roof when wading. During submersion the fan drives were disconnected and the radiator compartments sealed off and flooded. A bilge pump, mounted on the fighting compartment floor and driven by the power take-off from the main gearbox which also drove the power transverse oil pump, was used to pump out any water that penetrated the sealing devices. These vehicles could stay under water for 2½ hours. The idea of making the vehicle fully immersible was to leave it independent of bridges in a fast moving battle.

Anatomy of the Tiger

In the Tiger one of the biggest advances over any previous design was the method of construction. In order to simplify assembly as much as possible and allow the use of heavy armour plate, flat sections were used throughout the hull. Machinable quality armour plate was employed. Hull and superstructure were welded throughout, in contrast to previous German tanks where a bolted joint was used between hull and superstructure. The Tiger front and rear superstructure was in one unit, and interlocking stepped joints, secured by welding, were used in the construction of both the lower hull and the superstructure. A pannier was formed over each track by extending the superstructure sideways to full width and the complete length of the vehicle was so shaped from front vertical plate to tail plate. The top front plate of the hull covered the full width of the

The massive box-like hull, huge gun and mantlet of the Tiger are well shown from the front. The hull machine gun has been removed on this vehicle.

vehicle and it was this extreme width which permitted a turret ring of 6ft 1in internal diameter to be fitted which was of sufficient size to accommodate the breech and mounting of the 8·8cm gun. The belly was also in one piece, being a plate 26mm thick and 15ft 10¼in long by 5ft 11in wide.

Internally the hull was divided into four compartments, a forward pair housing the driver and the bow gunner/wireless operator, a centre fighting compartment and rear engine compartment. The driver sat on the left and steered by means of a wheel which acted hydraulically on the Tiger's controlled differential steering unit. Emergency steering was provided for by two steering levers on either side of the driver operating disc brakes. These brakes were also used for vehicle parking and were connected to a foot pedal and parking brake lever. A visor was provided for the driver and this was opened and closed by a sliding shutter worked from a handwheel on the front vertical plate. Fixed episcopes were provided in both the driver's and the wireless operator's escape hatches. A gyro direction indicator and instrument panel were situated to the left and right of the driver's seat respectively.

The gearbox separated the two forward crew members' compartments. The machine-gunner/wireless operator seated on the right manned a standard 7·92mm MG 34 in a ball mounting in the front vertical plate; this was fired by a hand trigger and sighted by a cranked telescope. The wireless sets were mounted on a shelf to the operator's left. The centre fighting compartment was separated from the front compartments by an arched cross member from the engine compartment in the rear by a solid bulkhead. The floor of the fighting compartment was suspended from the turret by three steel tubes and rotated with the turret. The breech mechanism of the 8·8cm gun reached almost to the inside rear turret wall, virtually dividing the fighting compartment in two.

The Weapons The 8·8cm KwK 36 gun which formed the Tiger's main armament had ballistic characteristics similar to those of the famous Flak 18 and Flak 36 8·8cm guns from which it was derived. The principal modifications were the addition of a muzzle brake and electric firing by a trigger operated primer on the elevating hand wheel. A 7·92mm MG 34 was co-axially mounted in the left side of the mantlet and was fired by mechanical linkage from a foot pedal operated by the gunner. The 8·8cm had a breech of the semi-automatic falling wedge type scaled up from the conventional type used on smaller German tank guns. The great weight of the barrel was balanced by a large coil spring housed in a cylinder on the left front of the turret. Elevation and hand traverse were controlled by handwheels to the right and left of the gunner respectively and an additional traverse handwheel was provided for the commander's use in an emergency. The hydraulic power traverse was controlled by a rocking footplate operated by the gunner's right foot. Because of the turret's great weight, traverse was necessarily low geared both in hand and power. It took 720 turns of the gunner's handwheel, for instance, to move the turret through 360 degrees and power traverse through any large arc demanded a good deal of footwork (and concentration) by the gunner. 'Stalking' Allied tanks – more lightly armoured – were often able to take advantage of this limitation to get in the first shot when surprising a Tiger from the side or rear. For sighting purposes the gunner was provided with a binocular telescope, a clinometer for use in HE shoots, and a turret position indicator dial. Ammunition for the 8·8 cm gun was stowed partly in bins each side of the fighting compartments and partly alongside the driver and under the turret floor.

Early production Tigers were fitted with 'S' mine dischargers on top of the superstructure, a total of five being mounted in various positions on the front, sides and rear. These devices were

The most notable and most highly decorated Tiger tank commander, Untersturmfuhrer Michel Wittmann of 1st SS-Pz-Div Leibstandarte SS 'Adolf Hitler' (*left*) with his crew. The 8·8 cm gun barrel carries a total tally of 88 'kills' of enemy tanks.

A company of Tiger tanks waiting to move forward at Tarnopol in early 1943. Because of re-supply difficulties on the Russian Front, they each carry extra drums of fuel.

installed for protection against infantry attacking with such anti-tank weapons as magnetic mines or pole charges. The 'S'-mine was a pot-shaped, anti-personnel bomb about 5in deep and 4in wide; it was shot some three to five feet into the air where it was set to explode and scatter its contents – 360 three-eighths inch steel balls.

The Turret Like the hull the turret was a simple structure; the sides and rear were formed from a single 82mm plate curved horseshoe fashion. The front was joined by two rectangular bars, 100mm thick, which were dovetailed and welded to the main turret front plate. The upper and lower edges of the turret sides converged towards the front to allow for movement of the mantlet when the gun was elevated or depressed. The turret roof was a single shaped plate 26mm thick, bent slightly forward of the centre line to match the taper of the sides at the front. This roof was recessed and welded into the turret sides. Two types of cupola could be seen fitted to Tigers; the original type had five vision slits and was of plain cylindrical appearance, while the later type had six episcopes and was exactly similar to the type fitted to the Panther.

In late 1943 Panther production was under way and several fittings such as cupolas and wheels were common to both the Tiger and Panther. Other external turret fittings were three NbK 39 90mm smoke generators on either side towards the front and two stowage bins either side of the centre line at the rear. The bins were used to stow the bedding, rations,

packs and other personal effects of the crew. In later production Tigers, the bins were often omitted, or only one fitted.

The Henschel Tiger was arguably the best quality tank ever put into mass production. It was extremely expensive to build and made heavy demands on man-hours. Very elaborate machine tools of enormous size were needed for the drilling and boring for the various fixtures and vast jigs were needed to handle the hulls during assembly work. No subsequent design could enjoy such lavish engineering, for as the war progressed quantity took precedence over quality.

Unit cost per vehicle was RM 250800, weapons excluded.

The Tiger in Service

It was intended to use the Tiger as a heavy infantry or assault Tank and Tiger battalions were organized as independent units under GHQ troops. Armoured divisions engaged in a major operation would receive an allotment of Tigers to spearhead an attack, but owing to the Tiger's basic lack of manoeuvrability due to its bulk and relatively low speed, it was always considered necessary to employ lighter tanks in supporting platoons on the flanks. Normally PzKpfw IIIs or IVs fulfilled this function. It was later decided to include Tigers in the basic organization of armoured divisions, but due to attrition which depleted the number of serviceable Tigers at any one time, it was never possible to put this plan into operation except in Waffen-SS armoured formations. These divisions were among the first units to receive Tigers, which went into service with such famous formations as the 1st SS Panzer Division Leibstandarte SS 'Adolf Hitler', and the 2nd SS Panzer Division 'Das Reich'. The fact that there were never sufficient Tigers to go round was probably the greatest comfort that opposing forces could take from their appearance.

In the earliest Tiger actions of the war, on the Russian Front before Leningrad and in Tunisia, the employment of these formidable and sinister looking vehicles was restricted to such limited numbers that resolute action by anti-tank gunners taking full advantage of the situation was more than enough to counter their impact. The first attack by Tigers in Russia in 1942 took place on terrain unsuitable for any successful tank action and, restricted to single file progress on forest tracks through the swamps, the Tigers proved easy targets for the Soviet gunners posted to cover the tracks.

The British first encountered the Tiger in February 1943, near Pont du Fahs in Tunisia. Having received advance warning of the im-

Right and top right The
Tiger I, Pz.Kpfw.VI
Ausf E.
Above Panzerjager VI,
Elefant.

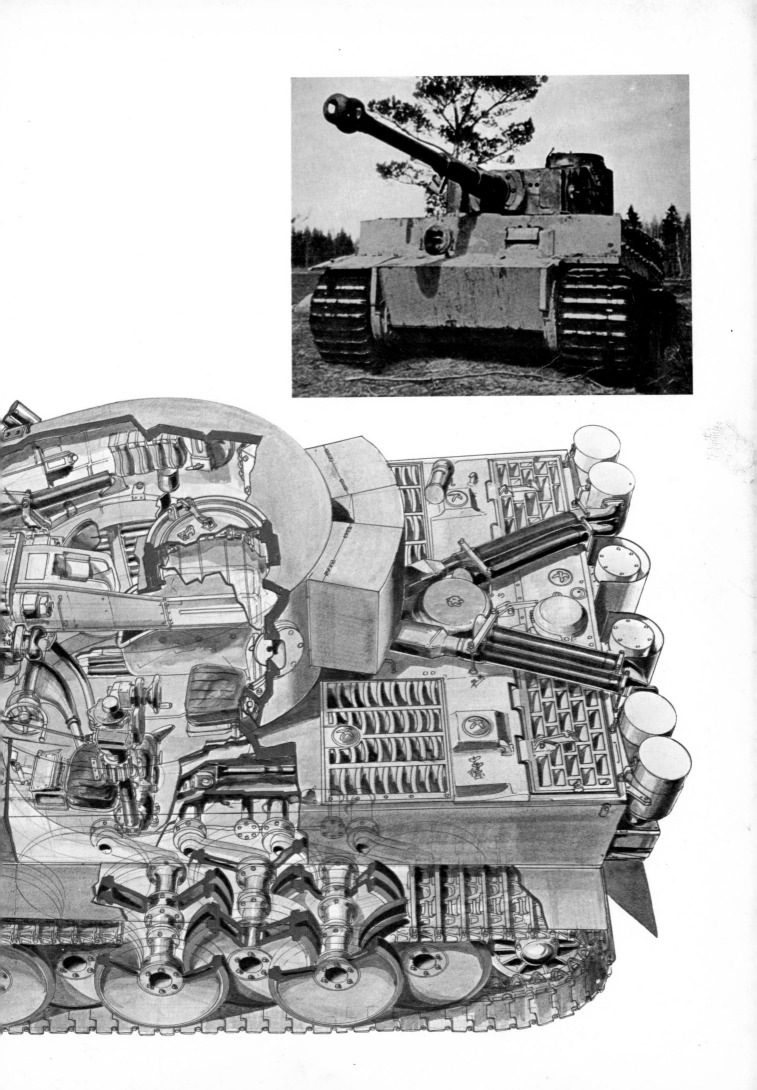

pending attack, the British anti-tank gunners were concealed with their 6pdrs with instructions to hold their fire until signalled. Two Tigers, flanked by nine PzKpfw IIIs and PzKpfw IVs advanced with artillery support and were not engaged until the range had closed to 300 yards on each flank. Fire from the 6pdr anti-tank battery knocked out both Tigers.

Tiger Variants

Three Tiger Ausf.E variants are known to have been in service.

(1) Tiger Command Tank (Panzerbefehls-wagen).

Designated Pz.Bef.Wg Tiger Ausf.E, this version was the normal fighting tank adapted for the fitting of additional wireless equipment. Two sub-variants existed of this Command Tank, SdKfz 267 and SdKfz 268, the difference between these two models being solely in the wireless equipment fitted. The SdKfz 267 carried combinations of the Fu 5 and Fu 8 radio and the SdKfz 268 was fitted with combinations of the Fu 5 and Fu 7.[1]

To accommodate the extra wireless equipment, the co-axial machine gun together with its ammunition, spares and tools were dispensed with and the ammunition for the 8·8cm gun was reduced by 26 rounds. The crew of five consisted of Commander, Wireless Officer (Gunner), W/T Operator I (Loader) W/T Operator II (Hull Gunner) and Driver.

(2) Pz.Kpfw Tiger Recovery Vehicle (Berg Pz.Wg.Tiger).

This was not standard equipment but is believed to have been a field workshop modification. It was intended as a towing vehicle for assisting crippled AFVs back to an area where repairs could be effected. It consisted of a normal Tiger modified by the removal of the 8·8cm

gun and the mounting of a band-operated winch at the rear of the turret with a wire rope guide at the front. Although the gun and barrel sleeve were removed the mantlet was retained, the opening in its centre being covered by a circular plate with a central aperture for a machine gun.

(3) 38cm Raketenwerfer 61 auf Sturmmorser Tiger.

Also known as Sturmtiger, Sturmpanzer VI, or Sturmmorser, this weapon was developed to requirements from the German Army engaged in the heavy street fighting at Stalingrad and other similar places in Russia. The fighting troops had requested a self-propelled 21cm howitzer capable of following up the advancing troops and able to engage difficult targets with high angle fire. When development work was started on this project it was decided that the Tiger E chassis would be used, but it was found that no suitable gun of 21cm calibre was available. It was finally proposed to use the Raketenwerfer 61 L/54, a 38cm rocket projector that had been developed by the firm of Rheinmetall-Borsig as an anti-submarine weapon for the German Navy. A model of the Sturmtiger was first shown on October 20, 1943 and limited production began in August 1944, 10 Tigers being converted by the Berlin firm of Alkett.

The hull of the Sturmtiger was similar to that of the Tiger E, but a fixed turret was superimposed on the hull with a single plate extending upwards from the rear edge of the standard Tiger glacis plate and sloped at 43 degrees to the vertical. The sides extended upwards at 20 degrees to the vertical from the top edges of the normal tank superstructure sides, which they overlapped slightly. The rear plate started at the forward edge of the engine compartment top and was sloped at about 10 degrees. The fighting compartment was roofed in by 40mm thick

The massively armoured but short-lived Sturmtiger, based on the Tiger hull and armed with a rocket mortar.

[1] Fu (funkgerat) wireless equipment.
Fu 5: standard tank set for short-range communication.
Fu 7: standard ground–air co-operation equipment.
Fu 8: standard set for main divisional links (range 6 miles).

plate. The rocket projector, which was breech loaded, was mounted offset to the right of centre in the 6-in front plate, and fired a 5 ft long projectile weighing 761 lb to a maximum range of 6200 yards. A hand operated ammunition crane was mounted at the offside of the super-structure rear plate; this was used to lift the rockets from the supply vehicle and lower them through the roof ammunition hatch into the fighting compartment. There were stowage arrangements for 12 rockets inside the vehicle, six on either side of the compartment. The rockets were stowed horizontally and held in position by collapsible cradles. The roof inside the compartment was fitted with overhead rails to carry a hand operated winch that could be run from side to side to place rockets on the loading tray and also assist in the stowage of ammunition. The rocket was loaded by hand with the projector set at zero elevation, from a loading tray fitted with six rollers. This could be folded into the floor when not in use. Additional armament consisted of a ball-mounted MG 34 machine gun set into the front plate on the right side.

The Sturmtiger when combat loaded weighed 70 tons and carried a crew of seven comprising a commander, observer, and five men to operate the vehicle and projector.

Overall length:	20 ft 8½ in
Overall width:	12 ft 3 in
Overall height:	11 ft 4 in including crane
Speed:	13–23 mph
Range:	Road 87 miles; Cross Country 55 miles

These vehicles when completed were too late to be used in fighting on the Russian Front, but they were used in the west – with negligible effect. For the Sturmtiger proved most un-wieldy. Apart from the inherent slowness of the Tiger chassis, the slow rate of fire rendered the vehicle almost a liability. Those sent to provide fire support for attacks on the Allies were all picked off easily as they lumbered up to the front and few, if any, ever had a chance of firing the Raketenwerfer in anger.

The Ferdinand

The Ferdinand (or Elefant) the self-propelled panzerjager development of the Porsche Tiger design had its own unique operational career, and its expected moment of glory as a major

Elefant (or Ferdinand) was built on the hull of Porsche's original un-successful Tiger design.

new weapon in the Kursk offensive of July 1943 turned into a tactical disaster of some magni-tude.

The Porsche-designed prototype for the VK.4501 requirement, the unsuccessful con-tender in the competition for a 45 ton battle tank, was already in limited production at the time the contract for the new 45 tonner was given to Henschel. Dr Ferdinand Porsche was an auto-motive engineer of distinction – amongst other cars he had designed the Volkswagen – and his experience of designing large commercial and military vehicles in the past led him to consider that petrol-electric (gas-electric) transmission was the smoothest, most efficient drive system for a heavy tracked vehicle.

In the VK.3001 prototype which Porsche produced (called by him the Leopard) two air-cooled petrol engines were mounted side by side at the rear and drove a dynamo which powered electric traction motors coupled to the front sprocket wheels. Suspension was by a system of torsion bars. Developed to meet the VK.4501 (45 ton) requirement, the basic design was retained and a Krupp-designed turret was supplied for the VK.4501(P) trial models.

Porsche's VK.4501 proved to be beset with problems, mainly concerning the engine cool-ing and transmission. When the more conven-tional Henschel VK.4501 prototype was chosen for production, there were already 90 Porsche vehicles laid down, mainly as a safeguard against failure of the Henschel design. The Krupp turret for the VK.4501(P) was, however, util-ized on the Henschel Tiger model. Only two of the VK.4501 Porsche vehicles had actually been completed as tanks and in this form they had been designated PzKpfw VI, VK.4501(P), Tiger (P). Two other variants of the Porsche Tiger were projected but never materialized. These were a Ramm-Tiger, or 'dozer-tank' ordered for production by Hitler and visualized for street fighting and ramming enemy tanks, and a con-

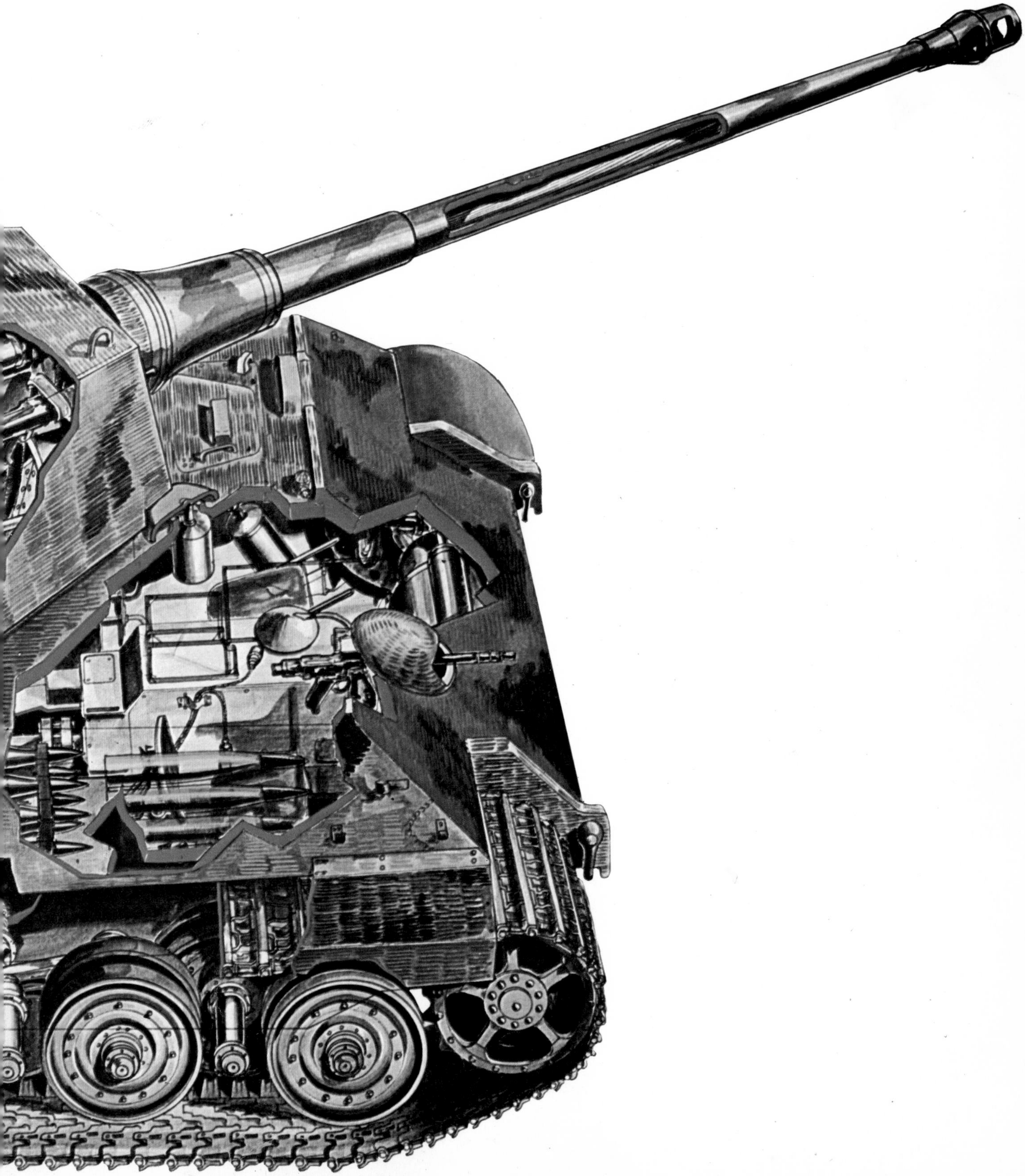

The Pz.Kpfw.VI (P)
Tiger II.

verted Porsche chassis designed to mount a 21 cm mortar.

Of the remaining vehicles under construction it was decided to utilize the chassis as the basis of a self-propelled carriage for the 8·8 cm L/71 gun. This equipment was designated Panzerjager Tiger (P) Ferdinand SdKfz 184; it was subsequently redesignated 8·8 cm 43/2 L/71 Ausf.Pz Jag Tiger (P) Elefant Früher Ferdinand. The original name 'Ferdinand' was adopted in honour of the designer.

Some 83 chassis were taken into hand for conversion to Ferdinands, the balance being converted to recovery vehicles. In essence the conversion entailed moving the engine and dynamo from the rear to the middle of the vehicle, thus leaving the rear end available for a fighting compartment and the 8·8 cm Pak 43/2 L/71 gun. This was in a limited transverse mount and the resulting vehicle was one of the biggest and, at 65 tons, heaviest produced up to that time, 1942. The Ferdinand looked almost impregnable as a fighting vehicle but it had serious deficiencies. The problem of doubtful mechanical reliability remained, and its tactical value was limited by poor visibility and, initially, the lack of a machine gun for close fighting.

The prototype vehicle was ready early in 1943 and production vehicles went to Panzer Regiment 654. In July of 1943 this unit was involved prominently in the Kursk Offensive, with disastrous results. The regiment was committed in force, but breakdowns took their toll, there was no defence against determined infantry attacks at close range, and the attack petered out and got bogged down after six miles. Many vehicles were lost to Russian hands, and with the Ferdinands cut off from their supporting tanks, the entire undertaking turned into a nightmare with a decisive defeat for the attackers.

After this debacle the few remaining Ferdinands, soon renamed Elefant, were given a hull machine gun for self-defence. These modified vehicles were used in odd numbers on the Italian front but played no significant part in any future tank action.

The Panther is Born

In his book *Panzer Leader*, General Heinz Guderian wrote:

'Numerous Russian T-34s went into action and inflicted heavy losses on the German tanks at Mzensk in 1941. Up to this time we had enjoyed tank superiority, but from now on the situation was reversed. The prospect of rapid decisive victories was fading in consequence. I made a report on this situation, which was for us a new one, and sent it to the Army Group; in this report I described in plain terms the marked superiority of the T-34 to our PzKpfw IV and

drew the relevant conclusion as that must affect our future tank production. I concluded by urging a commission be sent immediately to my sector of the front, and that it should consist of representatives of the Army Ordnance, the Armaments Ministry, the tank designers, and the firms that built tanks. If this commission was on the spot it could not only examine the destroyed tanks on the battlefield, but could also be advised by the men who had used them as to what should be included in the design for our new tanks. I also requested the rapid production of a heavy anti-tank gun with sufficient penetrating power to knock out the T-34. The commission appeared on the Second Panzer Army's front on November 20, 1941.'

The sudden decline in German panzer fortunes, brought about by the unexpected appearance of the revolutionary T-34 tank in Soviet hands, jolted the German Army Staff out of a complacency which had been caused entirely by the excellence and versatility of the conventional but efficient PzKpfw IV, which had been developed before the war.

The commission appointed by the Armaments Ministry acted swiftly. They made an 'on the spot' investigation on November 20, 1941, to assess the key features of the T-34 design. The three main characteristics of this vehicle which rendered all existing German tanks technically obsolete were (1) the sloped armour which gave optimum shot deflection all round, (2) the large road wheels which gave a stable and steady ride, and (3) the overhanging gun, a feature previously avoided by the Germans as impracticable. Of these the first was the most revolutionary. The Armaments Ministry acted promptly and on November 25, 1941, contracted with two principal armament firms, Daimler-Benz and MAN, to produce designs for a new medium tank in the 30–35 ton class, under the ordnance designation VK.3002. To be ready the following spring, the specifications called for a vehicle with 60 mm frontal armour and 40 mm side armour, the front and sides to be sloped as in the T-34. A maximum speed of 55 kmh (about 35 mph) was to be achieved.

In April 1942, the two designs, VK.3002 (DB)-DB: Daimler-Benz – and VK.3002 (MAN), were submitted to a committee of Waffenprufamt 6, the section of the Army Weapons Department (Heereswaffenamt) responsible for AFV design and procurement. The designs afforded an interesting contrast. The Daimler-Benz proposal was an almost unashamed copy of the T-34 in layout, with the addition of a few typical indigenous refinements. It had a hull shape similar to that of the T-34, with turret mounted well forward, so far forward in fact that the driver sat within the turret cage, with remote control hydraulic steering. A MB507 diesel engine was fitted with transmission to the rear sprockets again exactly duplicating the T-34 layout. Paired steel road wheels were suspended by leaf springs (a departure here from Christie suspension, but simpler and cheaper), and other features included escape hatches in the hull sides and jettisonable fuel tanks on the hull rear in the T-34 fashion. The VK.3002 (DB) was in fact a remarkably 'clean' design with much potential. Leaf springs, for example, were easier to produce than torsion bars, and the use of all-steel wheels recognized the problem of rubber shortage from the start. The compact engine and

tions for the driver and hull gunner/wireless operator in the front compartment.

Hitler always took a personal interest in AFV design and was on several occasions instrumental in ordering policy changes or design improvements. When the respective Daimler-Benz and MAN designs were submitted to the Waffenprufamt 6 committee in April 1942, Hitler was most impressed with the Daimler-Benz 'T-34 type' proposal, though he suggested that the gun be changed from the 7·5 cm L/48 model to the longer and more powerful L/70 weapon. Hitler's intervention in the proceedings at this stage led to an order for 200 VK.3002 (DB) vehicles being placed, and prototypes

The first production model Panther, PzKpfw V Ausf D, characterised by the opening ports for machine gunner and driver in the glacis plate.

transmission at the rear left the fighting compartment unencumbered for future up-gunning or structural change, while the diesel engine itself would have been an advantage in later years when petrol supply became acutely restricted.

By comparison, the VK.3002 (MAN) displayed original German (rather than Russian) thinking; it was sophisticated rather than simple. It had a higher wider hull than either the VK.3002 (DB) or the T-34, with a large turret placed well back to offset as much as possible the overhang of the long 7·5 cm gun which was called for as the main armament. Torsion bar suspension was used with interleaved road wheels, while a Maybach HL.210 petrol (gasoline) V-12 engine was proposed, with drive to the front sprockets. The internal layout followed conventional German practice with sta-

actually went into production. However, the committee set up by Waffenprufamt 6 – which was already being called unofficially the 'Panther Committee' – preferred the VK.3002 (MAN) design, because it was far more conventional by existing German engineering standards. MAN's proposal was accepted in May 1942 and they were asked to go ahead and produce a mild steel prototype as fast as possible. Subsequently, later in 1942, the order for the 200 Daimler-Benz vehicles was discreetly rescinded.

Meanwhile Ing. Kniepkampf, chief engineer and designer of Waffenprufamt 6, took personal charge of detail design work on the MAN vehicle. This reflected the priority given to the Panther project. Kniepkampf was a key figure in German AFV design at this time, having been with Waffenprufamt 6 since 1936 and remaining as chief engineer almost until the

Development of the
British cruiser tank.
Bottom Covenanter of
1940.
Opposite bottom Crusader
of 1941.
Right Centurion Mk III
of 1950.

war's end in 1945. Among other things he was principally responsible for German half-track development and introduced features like interleaved road wheels, torsion bar suspension, and the Maybach-Olvar gearbox to German tanks.

In September 1942 the first pilot model of the VK.3002(MAN) was completed and tested in the MAN factory grounds at Nuremburg. This was closely followed by the second pilot model which was transported to the Heereswaffenamt test ground at Kummersdorf for official army trials. By this time, incidentally, the Tiger was just in production, but its shortcomings – including excessive weight, low speed, and poor ballistic shape – were already recognized. The new vehicle was ordered into immediate pro-

duction as the PzKpfw V Panther, under the ordnance designation Sd Kfz 171, with absolute top priority rating. The first vehicle was turned out by MAN in November 1942. It was planned to build at a rate of 250 vehicles a month as soon as possible, but at the end of 1942 this target was increased to 600 a month. To reach such an ambitious target it was necessary to form a large Panther production group. Daimler-Benz were quickly switched from work on their now-discarded design (prototypes of which had by then been almost completed) and in November 1942 they, too, began tooling up to build Panthers, the first vehicles coming from Daimler early in 1943. Also in January 1943, Maschinenfabrik Niedersachsen of Hanover, and Henschel, began tooling up to build Panthers – production started in February/March – and scores of sub-contractors were soon involved in what became one of the most concentrated German armaments programmes of the war. Even aircraft production was cut back, partly to conserve fuel for use in tanks, but partly to free manufacturing facilities for Panther engines and components.

The monthly target of 600 vehicles was never achieved, however. By May 1943 output had reached a total of 324 completed vehicles and

PzKpfw V Panther Ausf A, showing the ball-mount for hull machine gun, driver's vision port, and side skirts.

Final production model, Panther Ausf G, had driver's vision port eliminated and episcope substituted. Note the Zimmerit anti-magnetic finish.

the monthly production average over the year was 154. In 1944 a monthly production average of 330 vehicles was achieved. By February 1945, when production tailed off, 4814 Panthers had been built. Panthers were first used in action in the great Kursk Offensive of July 5, 1943, but the haste with which the design had been evolved, and the speed with which it had been put into production led to many 'teething' troubles. In particular the complicated track and suspension gave trouble, with frequent breakages, while the engine presented cooling problems and this led to frequent engine fires. In the early months of service, indeed, more Panthers were put out of service by mechanical faults than by Soviet anti-tank guns.

There were three basic production models of the Panther, Ausfuhrung D, A, and G, in that order. The differences between them are explained later.

Anatomy of the Panther

The Panther conformed to the usual layout of German tanks. It had the driving and transmission compartment forward, the fighting compartment and turret in the centre, and the engine compartment at the rear. The driver sat on the left hand side forward with a vision port in front of him in the glacis plate. This was fitted with a laminated glass screen and had an armoured hinged flap on the outside which was closed under combat conditions. Forward vision was then given by two fixed episcopes in the compartment roof, one facing directly forward while the other faced half left in the '10.30' position. This restricted vision considerably and in the later Ausf G a rotating periscope was fitted in place of the fixed forward episcope, and the half left episcope and the vision port were completely dispensed with. The Ausf G was thus easily recognized from the front since it had an unpierced glacis plate. The wireless operator, who was also the hull machine gunner, sat on the right side forward. In the early Ausf D models, he was provided with a vertical opening flap in the glacis plate – rather similar to a vertical 'letterbox' flap – through which he fired a standard MG 34 machine gun in action. In the Ausf A and G, however, this arrangement was replaced by an integral ball-mount which took the MG 34 in the standard type of tank mounting. The radio equipment was fitted to the operator/gunner's right and was located in the sponson which overhung the tracks. Episcopes were fitted, duplicating the driver's side. Between the driver and wireless operator was

Panther Ausf D command tank with extra radio aerials and marked as a battalion commander's vehicle.

Following pages: Comet tanks of the British 7th Armoured Division (Divisional HQ Squadron) passing through the German town of Halle in 1947. The commander's cupola, vane sight, crew periscopes, and mushroom ventilator are well shown on the turret top of the leading vehicle.

located the gearbox, with final drive led each side to the front sprockets. The gearbox was specially evolved for the Panther as this vehicle was bulkier and heavier than previous designs and developed considerably more power. Known as the AK 7-200, the gearbox was an all synchromesh unit with seven speeds. Argus hydraulic disc brakes were used for steering in the conventional manner by braking the tracks. However, the epicyclic gears could also be used to assist steering by driving one or other of the sprockets against the main drive, so retarding the track on that side and allowing sharper radius turns.

In the turret the gunner sat on the left hand side of the gun and was originally provided with an articulated binocular sight; this was later changed to a monocular sight. He fired the gun electrically by a trigger fitted on the elevating handwheel. The co-axial machine gun, fitted in the mantlet, was fired by the gunner from a foot switch. Traverse was by hydraulic power or hand, the same handwheel being used for either method.

The vehicle commander's station was at the left rear of the turret, the offset location being necessitated by the length of the breech which

virtually divided the turret into two. A prominent cupola was provided which was of the 'dustbin' type with six vision slits in the Ausf D. In the Panther Ausf A and G, however, an improved cupola was fitted which had seven equally-spaced periscopes. This had a hatch which lifted and opened horizontally. Above the cupola was fitted a ring mount for a MG 34 which could be used for air defence, though this mount was sometimes removed.

The remaining crew member was the loader who occupied the right side of the turret. The turret itself had sloped walls and a rounded front covered by a curved cast mantlet. The cage had a full floor which rotated with the turret. Drive for the hydraulic traverse was taken through the centre of the floor to a gearbox, and thence to a motor. Turret openings were kept to a minimum and included a large circular hatch on the rear face which was an access/escape hatch for the loader and was also used for ammunitioning. On the left side beneath the cupola was a circular hatch for ejecting expended cartridge cases and re-ammunitioning, but this was eliminated in the Ausf A and G. Similarly eliminated were three small pistol ports, one in each face, which were normally plugged by a

Knocking out a Panther. Infantrymen surround a burning Panther just hit by a US Army tank destroyer. The inset picture shows an infantry squad rushing forward to capture a Panther just immobilized by the Bazooka rocket launcher team in the foreground.

steel bung and chain when not in use.

The engine, housed in the rear compartment, was a Maybach HL 230 P30, a V-12 23 litre unit producing 700hp at 3000rpm. This was a bored out version of the HL 210 engine originally planned. The earliest production vehicles had this unit, but like most AFV designs, the Panther had increased in weight considerably during the development stage with a heavier gun and heavier armour (among other things) bringing its weight up from the 35 tons originally envisaged to about 43 (metric) tons. The easy way to increase the power to compensate for the added weight was to enlarge the engine. Access to the engine for maintenance was via a large inspection hatch in the centre of the rear decking. Cooling grilles and fans occupied most of the remainder of the rear decking. Exhaust was taken away through manifolds on the squared off hull rear. Most Panthers had stowage boxes flanking the rear exhaust pipes, but these were not always fitted.

The actual hull and superstructure was a single built-up unit of machinable quality homogeneous armour plate of welded construction but with all main edges strengthened by mortised interlocking. The heaviest armour, 80mm, was on the glacis plate which was sloped at 33 degrees to the horizontal, an angle specifically selected to deflect shells striking the glacis upwards clear of the mantlet.

The suspension consisted of eight double inter-leaved bogie wheels on each side, the wheels being dished discs with solid rubber tyres. Some very late production vehicles, however, had all-steel wheels of the type fitted to the Tiger II (Royal Tiger), as described later. The first, third, fifth, and seventh wheels from the front were double while the intervening axles carried spaced wheels overlapping the others on the inside and outside. Each bogie axle was joined by a radius arm to a torsion bar coupled in series to a second bar laying parallel to it. The torsion bars were carried across the floor and the bogie wheels on the right hand side of the vehicle were set behind their respective torsion bars while those on the left were set in front. Thus the wheel layout was not symmetrical. This suspension was technically advanced and gave the vehicle superb flotation, but maintenance was complicated due to the size of the wheels and consequent inaccessibility of the axles and torsion bars. In addition wheel replacement was a heavy and lengthy task.

The 7·5cm L/70 gun mounted in the Panther was developed by Rheinmetall-Borsig who had been asked in July 1941 to design a high velocity version of the 7·5cm weapon which could penetrate 140mm of armour plate at 1000 metres. Soon after this the firm were asked to design the

turret and mount to hold this gun for installation in the VK.3002 design. The prototype gun, a weapon 60 calibres long, was ready in early 1942. Test firing indicated that performance was a little below the requested minimum, so the barrel was lengthened to 70 calibres, the improved prototype being ready for tests in June 1942. In this lengthened form the gun went into production. Initially it had a single baffle muzzle brake – and was so used on the earliest Panthers – but later a double baffle muzzle brake was adopted.

Panther Production Models

The first Panther models which came off the MAN line from November 1942 were designated PzKpfw V Ausf D.

Characteristics of the Ausf D were the 'dustbin' cupola, the vision port and machine gun port on the glacis, smoke dischargers on the turret sides, and a straight edge to the lower sponson sides with separate stowage compartments fabricated beneath the rear ends. On later Ausf Ds the improved type of cupola was fitted and the smoke dischargers were dropped in favour of a bomb thrower installed in the turret roof and operated by the loader. Later Ausf Ds also had the skirt armour, which was adopted as standard to protect the top run of the tracks from 'bazooka' hits, and Zimmerit anti-magnetic paste covering to prevent the attachment of mines. All except the earliest vehicles had the L/70 gun with double baffle.

Next production model of the Panther was designated Ausf A, and featured several detail improvements. Chief among these was the adoption of the new cupola with armoured periscopes, and the provision of a proper ballmount for the hull machine gun. Side skirts of 5mm armour and a Zimmerit finish were standard. The side skirts, incidentally, were only loosely fixed by bolts and they were frequently removed, either by the crew or by adjacent foliage in combat conditions. The gunner's binocular sight was replaced by a monocular one, though this was not noticeable externally. To further simplify turret production, however, the pistol port and the small loading hatch featured in the Ausf D were eliminated completely, leaving just the big loading/escape hatch in the turret rear. The Panther Ausf A was the main type encountered by the Allies in the Normandy fighting.

The final production model of the Panther in its original form was also in action in Normandy in June 1944. This was the Ausf G. By this time the designation PzKpfw V had been dropped following a personal directive from Hitler on February 27, 1944, and the vehicle was simply known as the Panther Ausf G. Considerable

Panthers come under artillery barrage fire during an attack on the Russian Front.

modifications featured in this vehicle. The superstructure sides were altered, mainly to simplify production, so that the rear stowage compartments were now integral with the hull instead of separate additions. This gave a sloping lower edge to the sponsons. The hull sides were at the same time increased in thickness from 40mm to 50mm with the angle of slope altered from 30 degrees to 40 degrees. The driver's vision port was eliminated from the glacis plate and his vision was greatly improved by provision of a rotating periscope in place of the episcopes. New hinged hatches with spring-assisted opening replaced the original hatches provided in the hull roof for the driver and wireless operator. The earlier models had pivoted hatches which were found to jam easily. Internally, armoured ammunition bins were fitted inside each sponson with sliding armoured doors to reduce fire risk. The 7·5 cm ammunition stowage was also slightly increased in this model, from 79 to 82 rounds.

The Panther II

With the Tiger and Panther being produced, a new generation of tanks was planned which was to incorporate the lessons from existing designs. In particular, most urgent attention was to be given to simplifying production, economizing on materials, reducing maintenance, and standardizing components as far as possible. In February 1943 Waffenprufamt 6 asked MAN and Henschel to produce improved designs for the Panther and Tiger respectively, ensuring maximum interchange-

ability of parts. Henschel produced the Tiger II (or King Tiger) which went into production at the end of 1943 since a replacement for the somewhat unsatisfactory and expensive Tiger was the main priority. The improved Panther, the Panther II, officially designated Panther Ausf F, was to have a hull similar to the existing Panther but with the same form of interleaved all-steel resilient wheels as the Tiger II. Other changes were to be the adoption of an improved gearbox and transmission, the AK 7-400, and mechanical parts such as brakes identical to those in the Tiger II. The armour on the hull top was to be doubled to 25 mm and the ball-mount was to be altered to take the MG 42. The major change, however, was to be a new design of turret, known as the Panzerturm Schmal (small), which, as its name implies, was much smaller than the original Panther turret. The object was to reduce weight, simplify production, reduce frontal area, eliminate shot traps beneath the mantlet (a weakness in the original Panther turret) and enable a larger gun to be fitted. It was to have a built-in stereoscopic rangefinder, and a gyrostabilizer for both the sight and the gun based on that fitted in American tanks. As part of the experimental work for this a standard Panther was fitted with a gyrostabilizer for firing trials, when accuracy and effectiveness was proved to be doubled.

The new small turret was developed as a separate project by Daimler-Benz under the direction of Dr Wunderlich, assisted by Col. Henrici, a gunnery expert from Waffenprufamt 6. Kniepkampf was in overall charge of both the

Tiger II and Panther II projects. The new turret proved a most successful design. It had the same ring diameter as the old turret, but took 30 per cent less time to make and had 30 per cent more armour plate, all within the same weight limit. It could take the L/70 gun, was also designed to accommodate a proposed lengthened L/100 version of the same weapon, and could take the same 8·8 cm gun as the Tiger II as yet another alternative. The wide mantlet, difficult to manufacture, which characterized the old turret, was replaced by a relatively simple Saukopf (pig's head) mantlet, of conical shape as its description implies. The turret was ready before the Panther II, but although running prototypes of this vehicle were produced in 1944, the rapidly deteriorating conditions of the war with facilities curtailed and the need for continued supply of types already proven meant that the Panther II, or Ausf F, never went into production. There was thus no chance for this fine design, virtually a perfected version of the original Panther, to prove its mettle. It would have undoubtedly been a much more useful and potent weapon than the very heavy and bulky Tiger II.

Final production models of the Panther Ausf G did, in fact, incorporate one feature intended for the Ausf F. This was the all-steel resilient road wheel which replaced the rubber tyred type and became standard for late-production Tigers as well as the Tiger II.

Other Panther Projects

By late 1944, several advanced projects based on the Panther chassis were in the design stage.

Of these the most important were an AA tank, a Waffentrager, a minesweeper tank, and a dozer tank. For the Panther II chassis a Panzerjager SP variant was proposed incorporating a 12·8 cm gun, the largest possible weapon which could be fitted on the chassis. Because of the war situation, however, few of these projects got beyond the mock-up stage, though the Waffentrager existed as a single prototype. A further development associated with the Panther which did see service was infra-red night fighting equipment. A number of Panthers were actually fitted experimentally with infra-red sights and these operated in conjunction with a 60 cm infra-red searchlight carried on an accompanying half-track vehicle called the Uhu (Eagle Owl). The Uhu could 'illuminate' targets at 1000 metres and the Panther could pick out this target on closing to 500 metres.

Panther Variants

There were several special purpose conversions of the Panther, two of these for the command role. For unit commanders the Befehlspanzer Panther was produced. These were simply versions of either the Ausf D, A or G fitted with extra radio equipment and the associated aerials. A second wireless receiver and transmitter were fitted to the inside right wall of the turret and the loader acted as operator. There were two externally similar models, differing only in the radio installation. The Sd Kfz 267 had Fu 5 and Fu 8 equipment, while the Sd Kfz 268 had Fu 5 and Fu 7. In each case ammunition stowage was reduced to 64 7·5 cm rounds. Befehlspanzer Panthers were used by regimental and battalion

Winch and jib replaced the turret in the Bergepanther recovery vehicle. Note the earth spade at rear.

The superb Jagdpanther tank destroyer.

command and staff officers and could only be distinguished externally by the extra aerials (or the call sign number when this was visible).

The Beobachtungspanzer Panther (Sd Kfz 172) was an old Ausf D converted as an OP vehicle for observation officers, commanders and staff officers of SP artillery regiments. The gun was replaced by a short wooden dummy, the turret was fixed in place, an extra wireless was fitted, and a map table was added inside the turret. A ball-mounted MG 34 in the turret front was the only armament.

Finally, there was the Bergepanzer Panther (also known as the Bergepanther), designated Sd Kfz 179, which was a recovery vehicle specially for work with tanks in the 45 ton class. The Bergepanther replaced the 18 ton half-track in the heavy recovery role, since it took up to three of those vehicles to move heavy tanks like the Tiger or Panther. The Bergepanther was an old Ausf D model converted by the removal of the turret and the fighting equipment. A movable winch and winch motor were installed in the fighting compartment. A limited super-structure was provided round the former turret opening consisting of heavy wood cladding over mild steel framing. A canvas tilt could cover the complete compartment in inclement weather. An 'A' frame was fitted over the rear decking and this supported a towing eye and towing rollers. A heavy earth spade was hinged on the hull rear and was raised and lowered from the vehicle's winch. There was a light demount-able jib which could be erected either side for lifting work and there was either an MG 34 or 2 cm cannon for air defence, mounted as re-quired. Design and conversion of the Berge-panther was carried out by Demag and 297 vehicles were so altered. Not all of these were fitted with earth spades, however, and these were used as towing vehicles. Some of the Bergepanthers without spades later had their winches removed and were used as munition carriers. Some other old Panthers simply had their turrets removed and were also used as munition carriers.

The Jagdpanther

The most important derivative of the Panther, however, was the famous Jagdpanther, one of the best-known AFVs to appear during the Second World War. The Germans built several important items of self-propelled artillery equipment as assault guns or tank destroyers but invariably these were makeshift adaptations on obsolescent, if not obsolete, chassis. The need for a fast, up-to-date tank destroyer on a modern chassis was met by adapting the Panther.

Previous attempts to produce a heavy tank destroyer had been largely unsuccessful. The 8·8 cm Pak had already been mounted on the Porsche Tiger chassis (to make the Ferdinand) and on the PzKpfw III/IV chassis as the Nashorn, but both of these improvisations proved unsatisfactory – the Ferdinand was too heavy and the Nashorn was too small and underpowered. By 1943, however, there was an urgent need for tank destroyers in quantity, so it was decided to utilize the best available chassis, that of the Panther. MIAG were asked to work out the design and the prototype was first demonstrated, in the presence of Hitler, on October 20, 1943.

The Panther chassis was used unaltered, but the front and upper side plates were extended upwards to make a well-sloped enclosed super-structure. The mantlet was fitted in the centre of the hull front with a limited traverse for the 8·8 cm Pak 43/3 L/71 gun of 11 degrees each side. Armour was 80mm in front and 60mm at the sides. A ball-mounted MG 34 was fitted in the right front and the driver sat in the usual position in the left front. Sighting equipment consisted of a rangefinder and periscope tele-scope. The telescope protruded through a slot in the roof within an armoured quadrant arc linked to the gun mount.

The new SP version of the Panther was at first designated 8·8 cm Pak 43/3 auf Panzerjager Panther (Sd Kfz 173) but at Hitler's personal suggestion in February 1944 it was redesignated simply as the Jagdpanther (Hunting Panther).

MIAG commenced building Jagdpanthers in February 1944, using the Ausf G chassis which had by then become the current production type. By the war's end 382 had been completed. The only mechanical change compared with the Panther tank was the provision of the AK 7-400 gearbox as was also earmarked for use in the Panther II. As already mentioned, a project existed for a Panzerjager version of the Panther II with 12·8 cm gun, this being drawn up in late 1944 but built only as a wooden mock-up.

Crew of the Jagdpanther consisted of a com-

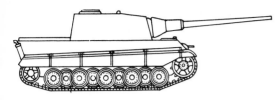

mander, gunner, two loaders, wireless operator/machine gunner and driver. The vehicle carried 60 8·8cm rounds.

The Jagdpanther was the best and most potent of all the German tank destroyers. It was well-shaped, low, fast and heavily armoured. The intention was to build Jagdpanthers at a rate of 150 per month, but disrupted production facilities in the last year of the war made this target quite impossible to achieve.

Had the war dragged on (and had Germany been able to maintain its planned production programme unhindered), the Panther, Panther II, and Jagdpanther would have become the backbone of the German panzer divisions (together with the Tiger II and Jagdtiger in lesser numbers), and from late 1944 a rationalization programme was introduced (Richtwert-Programm IV) which terminated production of all earlier types in favour of the 'new generation' vehicles. The other type to be included in the new programme was a family of Waffentragers and SP types developed on a light chassis adapted from the Czech-built PzKpfw 38(t), and its German-developed derivative, the 38(d).

However, cessation of hostilities in May brought the German tank story to a swift and premature close with much of the potential of the design still unrealized.

A few Panthers served on for a number of post-war years, however, but in the French Army which equipped some units with captured vehicles. The other victorious nations each took a few Panthers for trials. The British actually built at least one Panther in 1946, using spare and cannibalized parts to assemble a 'new' vehicle which was used in comparative trials with the new British Centurion tank.

The Tiger II

In chronological terms the last important German heavy tank was the Tiger Ausf B or Koenigstiger (King Tiger or Royal Tiger), also known as the Tiger II. It went into production in late 1943 and first saw service on the Eastern Front in May 1944, then was introduced on the Western Front in August 1944, following the Allied invasion of France.

The Tiger II was actually a new design, owing more to the Panther than the original Tiger design. It originated in August 1942 when the Ordnance Department issued a requirement for a Tiger replacement superior to the T-34 in armour protection and firepower. Porsche and Henschel submitted designs, Porsche adapting his original unsuccessful Tiger design. His final design submission, the VK. 4502(P) was considered and a batch of turrets was put in

JagPz VI 'Jagdtiger'
128mm

An early King Tiger with the Porsche turret, knocked out in Normandy, July 1944.

King Tigers on the firing range in late 1944. Note the commander's periscope sights emerging through the turret's roof hatch.

hand. The tank itself was abandoned, however, after acceptance, for it retained the petrol-electric drive feature favoured by Porsche, and copper required for the transmission parts was by this time in short supply.

Henschel, meanwhile, submitted a design based on the original Tiger but then modified it considerably at the Ordnance Department's request to incorporate all possible features from the projected Panther II design, the objective being to aim for maximum rationalization of parts and spares.

First production examples of the Henschel model were ready in February 1944, and 484 were built by the war's end. The first 50 used the more elegantly shaped Porsche turret, built for Porsche's intended design. The Henschel turret was less complicated, squared off at each end and simplified in shape as much as possible to facilitate mass production.

The Koenigstiger was one of the most massive and spectacular tanks ever built. All the good points of the Panther were incorporated, including the sloped armour. The gun was the big 8·8cm L/71, an improved longer version of the gun used in the original Tiger. Internally the vehicle followed the Panther layout almost exactly, but there was no turret basket and the vehicle was well provided with escape hatches. To facilitate loading with the heavy 8·8cm gun, 22 rounds were carried in racks at the rear of the turret ready for instant use, the noses of the rounds being close to the gun breech, requiring minimal movement for loading. Excellent vision devices were provided. The driver had a periscope in the hull roof and, in addition, could raise his seat and controls for normal 'on the march' driving with his roof hatch open. An episcope was provided for the hull machine gunner, with another in the turret roof for the loader. The gun had a monocular gun sight and the commander had a vision cupola of the type used in the late-model Panther. Radio, turret controls, and other fittings were as for the Panther. The armour protection was the thickest employed on a mass-produced tank up to that time. The glacis plate was 150mm thick, at 40 degrees, and the nose was 100mm thick, at

The definitive production model of the King Tiger with Henschel turret.

55 degrees. The hull and turret sides and back were 80mm thick and the top and belly plates were 42mm thick. Armour was of the interlocked type as on the Tiger. Most vehicles had a coating of Zimmerit anti-magnetic mine paste.

Suspension was by torsion bars and the wheels were overlapped, rather than interleaved as on the Panther and Tiger. This simplified maintenance and wheel changing. The wheels were all steel (with rubber resilient cushions) thus saving valuable tyre rubber. Like the Tiger I there were wide and narrow tracks.

A complementary development was the Jagdtiger with slightly lengthened suspension, but otherwise similar to the Tiger Ausf B. A big fixed superstructure replaced the turret, with a 12·8cm gun. In terms of weight, this was the biggest production vehicle to see service in the Second World War. The front plate armour was 250mm thick, sloped at 15 degrees, and made of one piece of solid cast steel. The superstructure sides were made integral with the hull sides and

were 80mm thick at 25 degrees (the slope in all cases quoted being measured from the vertical). Some 38 rounds of 12·8cm ammunition were carried, and the 12·8cm gun was the largest anti-tank gun used during the war.

The King Tiger's finest hour came in the Battle of the Bulge where it was used (with Panthers) to spearhead the classic December 1944 Ardennes Offensive against the Americans, which almost succeeded in splitting the Allied armies. Like the Tiger before it, however, the King Tiger was so big and so heavy that it was itself a tactical liability. It presented a big target and was too heavy for most road bridges. In a straight tank versus tank shooting match it could outrange almost any Allied tank while being nearly immune itself to Allied AP rounds. But in the war of movement of 1944 where the Allies had massive resources of fast moving armoured vehicles, and mastery of the air above the battlefield, it gave the German forces at best only limited advantages.

The massive Jagdtiger, the most heavily armed and armoured AFV of the Second World War.

Paratroops ride on a King Tiger in the opening stages of the 'Battle of the Bulge'.

The British Cruiser Tanks

One of the most interesting comparisons of all in the history of tank development is the contrasting results achieved by the two nations which placed their faith in Christie's fast tank design. On the one hand, as we have seen, the Soviets developed the basic Christie design via the BT to the T-34, and very largely got it right first time. They judged the best possible mix of firepower, mobility, and armour, and dispensed with the 'frills'. The T-34 was a spartan but clean design, easy to produce and maintain – in essence the Russians did not tamper with Christie's concept as first adopted. Simplicity was all.

The British had no such luck the first time they tried. It took most of the war years to produce a very satisfactory 'cruiser' (or medium) tank although the British, too, had started from the basis of one of Christie's prototypes. Study of the archives shows that the British tank designers fought their hardest battles in committees and on paper. A tremendous effort was put into some very promising designs, but the British designers worked against a barrage of ever-changing requirements, suggestions, inter-departmental strife, and several changes of supply and design organizations. British tanks of the time were very much designed 'by committees' and all too often, as is usually the case, the committees tended to lose sight of the objective. The inherent simplicity of the Christie design was soon forgotten and the British tanks became too complicated.

The A13 and A13 Mk II tanks, previously described (Chapter 3), were found to be quite successful, as we have seen. They were also quite simple and the closest to Christie's design in spirit. Tampering with the idea led to problems, as is evidenced by the sorry tale of the Covenanter tank of 1940.

This vehicle was one of several designs quite hastily put together in the period while the first British Christie type vehicles were being built. It was suggested that a new category of tank, the 'heavy cruiser', with 30mm armour and high speed, should be built to supplement the A13. This resulted in the A14 and A16 designs which were multi-turreted monsters, the former with side skirt armour. The prototype A14 was completed early in 1939 but it proved mechanically complicated, and too slow by comparison with an A13, even when the latter was loaded down with simulated 30mm armour. Hence it was decided to cancel the A15 and A16 contract and build instead an improved and better armoured version of the A13.

The work was entrusted to the London, Midland and Scottish Railway Co., which had been building the A14. The new 'heavy cruiser' was to use as many A13 parts as possible, but was to be built from the start with a 30mm armour basis, and it was to have a lower overall height. A wood mock-up was approved in April 1939.

To keep the profile to the desired low height, a Meadows flat-12 engine was fitted. Compared to the A13, the new model, designated A13 Mk III, later called Cruiser Tank Mark V, Covenanter, had its engine at the back with the radiators set alongside the driver. First production models were delivered early in 1940, but proved poor, due mainly to cooling problems. Many modifications were necessary, but the problems were never satisfactorily overcome.

A less serious problem was high ground pressure due to the increased weight of the vehicle. Nearly 2000 of these handsome vehicles were built but they were never used in combat.

The Crusader stemmed from the same line of development as the Covenanter. The original

A15 design for a '1938 Class Medium' was delayed in the planning stage due to uncertainties of requirements, and was redesignated A16 when Nuffields took on the project. Soon after approval of the A13 Mk III (Covenanter) mock-up was given in April 1939, the Director of Mechanization asked the General Staff to review the alternative designs then being considered for the standard 'heavy cruiser' role. These included the A18 (a larger development of the Tetrarch light tank), the A14 (being developed by the LMS), the A16 (being developed by Nuffields), and the 'new' A15, which was a proposed enlarged development of the A13 Mk III. The A15 emerged as the favoured design because (a) it utilized a large number of components from the A13 series, including the Christie suspension, (b) it could therefore be got into production faster, (c) it offered a better trench crossing ability than the A13 Mk III due to its increased length, (d) it was to be built to a 40–30mm armour basis, which was much superior to that of the other contenders. Nuffields were asked to produce a detailed design, based on the A13 Mk III but lengthened by one bogie wheel each side. In June 1939, Nuffields suggested that they use the Liberty engine of the original A13 design instead of the Meadows engine of the A13 Mk III, since they already had the Liberty engine in production and this would obviate delays. Since it also kept the weight down, the Director of Mechanization agreed, and approval to go ahead was given in July 1939 with an initial order for 200 tanks plus the pilot model. This latter was ready by March 1940. In mid 1940 the order for A15s was increased to 400, then to 1062, and Nuffields became the 'parent' company to a group of nine companies engaged in A15 production. Total output until 1943 was 5300 vehicles.

'Teething' troubles with the pilot model included poor ventilation, inadequate engine cooling, and mechanical problems with the gear change.

Though most of the initial defects were overcome to an extent, the Crusader, as it was named in late 1940, always suffered from unreliability and the speed and urgency with which it was rushed into production did not allow long development trials, particularly for desert operations, where the Crusader became the principal British tank from Spring 1941 onwards. It first saw action near Capuzzo in June 1941, was prominent in all the major North African desert actions which followed, and was still in service, in its later form with a 6pdr as its principal armament at the time of the Battle of Alamein in October 1942, though by then it was being displaced by American-built M3 and M4 mediums. The last Crusaders in North Africa were finally withdrawn from first line use in May 1943, but the type was used for training until the end of the war. From the summer of 1942 onwards Crusaders were converted for numerous special purpose roles, including AA tanks, gun tractors, and ARVs. In the desert the Crusader so impressed the Italians that they proceeded to build a direct copy of the vehicle, which was still at prototype stage when the war ended.

The Crusader was designed just too soon to incorporate any of the lessons learned in the early tank actions in France in 1940, but several modifications resulted from trials with the prototype. These included removal of the front auxiliary machine gun turret, mainly because it was too poorly ventilated and of limited value, and this also simplified production. This turret was also removed retrospectively from many Mk I vehicles in service, and the space allowed extra ammunition stowage. It was also possible to increase the armour thickness slightly on hull and turret front. Finally, the Mk III version was

The Covenanter (*above left*), a vehicle of 1st Armoured Division in early 1941, and its successor, the Crusader (*above*): a Mk I is shown with the distinctive small auxiliary hull machine gun turret.

Crusaders in the Western Desert, November 1942, in the chase after the retreating Afrika Korps. Nearest vehicle is a Crusader Mk III with 6pdr gun. Note how the disruptive painting on the gun barrel breaks its outline.

Crusader AA Mk II of the Polish Armoured Division in August 1944; AA tanks were not used widely by the British as the Allies had mastery of the air at this time.

One of the last actions in which Crusaders took part as gun tanks; a Mk III is here shown approaching 'Two Tree Hill' during a notable incident at Bou Arada, Tunisia, January 10, 1943.

up-gunned with a 6pdr replacing the 2pdr.

The Germans respected the Crusader for its speed, but it was no match for the PzKw III with 50mm gun, its main desert opponent, in hitting power, armour thickness, or serviceability. The German 55mm, 75mm and 88mm anti-tank guns also had no trouble in picking off Crusaders in the desert fighting.

The main Crusader variants were:

Crusader I Original production model with 2pdr gun and auxiliary front machine gun turret, which was later removed on some vehicles in service.

Crusader I CS As above but with 3in howitzer replacing 2pdr gun for close support role.

Crusader II As Crusader I but with front machine gun turret eliminated during course of production programme. Extra frontal armour on turret and hull.

Crusader II CS As Cruiser I CS with improvements as for standard Mk II.

Crusader III Final production version with 6pdr gun replacing 2pdr weapon, and increased armour on hull and turret and other parts of hull. The prototype was tested during November and December 1941. It was in production from May 1942, and 144 were completed by July 1942.

Crusader III, AA Mk I Crusader III with turret removed and replaced by single Bofors 40mm AA mount. In early conversions the unmodified ground mount was used, but most had an all-round open-topped shield.

Crusader III, AA Mk II Crusader III with gun turret removed and replaced by new enclosed turret with twin 20mm Oerlikon AA cannon.

Crusader III, AA Mk III As AA Mk II but with radio equipment removed from turret and installed in hull front next to driver.

These AA versions were produced for the invasion of NW Europe in 1944, a troop of AA tanks being allotted to every HQ squadron. However, due to the Allied air superiority, and the consequent rarity of attacks by enemy aircraft, the AA troops were disbanded, shortly after the Normandy landings in June 1944.

Covenanter Bridgelayer Development of a 30ft 30 (long) ton folding ('scissors') bridge began in 1936 for mounting on a tank. Due to the availability and power of the Covenanter, a number of Mk I and Mk II vehicles were fitted with the production type of scissors bridge, which was laid by hydraulic rams and arms installed in the fighting compartment, with power taken from the engine fan drive. It was mainly used for training and development work, together with the Valentine Bridgelayer. The bridge was 34ft long overall and 9½ft wide.

From A24 to A27

The Covenanter and the Crusader pilot models plus the accrued lessons of the 1940 tank actions in France and Libya led the Ministry of Supply, at the end of 1940, to ask for a heavy cruiser tank which overcame the inherent faults of the existing designs. Thicker armour (65mm on hull front, 75mm on turret front), bigger turret ring (60in diameter), a heavier gun (6pdr), a more powerful engine, a weight limit of 24 tons, a speed of not less than 24mph, and above all much better mechanical reliability, were among the many improvements requested. In January 1941 the Tank Board considered proposals to meet these requirements. Vauxhall Motors offered a scaled-down version of the Churchill infantry tank, designated A23, which was not taken up, while Nuffield Mechanizations and Aero offered a design based upon that of the Crusader which they were already building. Mechanization and Aero were therefore asked to build six pilot vehicles for completion by the following autumn, under the designation A24. This vehicle was mechanically similar to the Crusader and was to retain the Liberty engine and Wilson epicyclic gearbox.

Meanwhile, Leyland Motors, one of the production group involved in building the Convenanter and Crusader, suggested a design which utilized a chassis similar to the Crusader but was powered with an adapted version of the Rolls-Royce Merlin aero engine and had the new Merritt-Brown gearbox already being used in the Churchill. However, at this period all Merlin production was needed for aircraft, but the basic chassis design of the A24 was rationalized with the Leyland design (then designated A27) and an order for 500 A24s was placed 'off the drawing board' in June 1941, and the name Cromwell I was allocated. The A24 was to be considered as an interim type while the Merlin-engined A27 was developed. It was then decided to reserve the name Cromwell for the A27 and the name Cavalier was given to the A24, first pilot model of which was eventually completed in January 1942.

With its Liberty V12 engine, the A24 Cavalier offered no mechanical advance over the Crusader and, in fact, due to the increased weight it had an inferior performance, shorter engine life, and was even more prone to break down. Production vehicles were used only for training as gun tanks, but in 1943 half were converted to OP tanks for artillery use and in this guise some were used by artillery regiments of armoured divisions in the NW Europe campaign of 1944–45. A few others were converted to ARVs.

The main feature of Leyland's A27 design was the famous Rolls-Royce Merlin aero engine, which in its form adapted for tank use was named the Meteor. With an output of 600bhp, this power unit gave ample performance for a

The celebrated Cromwell tank. This is a Mk IV with 75 mm gun and cowled exhaust. It is ready to fire from a bulldozed hull-down position, January 1945. Note the spare wheel and camouflaged turret. Unit badges have been deleted from photograph by a wartime censor.

tank in the heavy cruiser category, was a far superior engine to the Liberty (which dated basically to 1917), and was already in production for aircraft use which meant that valuable time was saved which would otherwise have been necessary for development work.

Birmingham Carriage and Wagon were asked to become 'parents' for the A27 and work out design details. However, due to the shortage of Merlin engines, needed for aircraft production, an interim version of the A27 was proposed, retaining the Liberty engine of the Crusader, but otherwise identical to the Merlin engined design. English Electric were asked in November 1941 to design this version, which was designated A27L (L: Liberty engine), Cromwell II. The Meteor-engined variant was to be called Cromwell III. Leyland took over production 'parentage' and the name was meanwhile changed to Centaur, the Cromwell name being kept exclusively for the Meteor-engined A27s. The A27L design had to be to the same dimensions as the Nuffield-designed Cavalier, but the Liberty engine installation had to be interchangeable with that for the Meteor power plant, to allow for replacement at a later date when Meteors became available in quantity. A Merritt-Brown gearbox was used instead of the epicylic gearbox (to conform with the Meteor-engined design), and other changes involved shifting the radiators to the rear of the same compartment and incorporating mechanical parts common to the Meteor-engined vehicle. The Centaur pilot model was completed in June

1942 and first production vehicles were ready by the end of the same year. About 950 were completed, 80 of them as close support models with a 95 mm howitzer in place of the 6 pdr gun. These were used on the D-Day landings by the Royal Marines Armoured Support Group, giving covering fire from LCTs and then landing over the beaches on June 6, 1944.

Known as Cromwell III, the Meteor-engined version of the A27 design was designated A27M (M: Meteor engine). In the Meteor engine adaptation of the Merlin for tank use about 80 per cent of the component parts were identical to the aircraft engine, thus greatly facilitating production for tanks. Rolls-Royce converted a batch of Merlins for use in tanks, and during 1941 two Crusader tanks had Meteor engines installed in place of their Liberty power plants for exhaustive test running. This enabled positioning of auxiliary components, wear and tear, oil consumption, and so on to be determined at an early date, while design work on the A27 itself proceeded. Birmingham Carriage and Wagon delivered the first mild steel prototype to the Army for trials on March 1, 1942, actually ahead of the Centaur pilot model. Two more pilot models were delivered by the end of 1942, and teething troubles on tests proved relatively minor – mainly detail points concerned with clutch, gears, and cooling. The idea of using the powerful Meteor engine was handsomely vindicated by results, and ample power was available for any foreseen developments of the A27 type. Cromwell production started in January 1943,

by which time Leyland had become the design and production 'parents' for the entire A27 series. This embraced all subcontractors for component parts as well as plants building Cromwells.

Meanwhile, War Office policy towards tank armament had changed considerably since the 'heavy cruiser' requirement resulting in the A24/A27 series had been formulated. Fighting in the Western Desert, coupled with the decisive appearance of the American-built M3 and M4 Medium tanks in that theatre, led to a requirement for a gun with 'dual-purpose' capability – able to fire HE or AP shot – as fitted in the very successful M3 and M4 mediums. Work on a British designed version of the 75 mm gun (virtually a bored-out development of the British 6pdr able to fire American ammunition) was put in hand in December 1942 and Cromwells from Mk IV onward were produced with this weapon in place of the 6pdr. The first vehicles so equipped were delivered in November 1943, but there were many initial defects in this gun, including unsatisfactory semi-automatic cams in the breech, which were not entirely put right until May 1944.

The Cromwell was numerically the most important British-built cruiser tank of the Second World War, forming the main equipment of British armoured divisions in 1944–45 together with the American-built M4 Sherman. However, even with a 75 mm gun it was, by 1944 standards, still inferior to contemporary German tanks like the Panther and late-model

PzPKw IVs. With its Meteor engine it was the fastest and most powerful of British tank designs until that period, but physical limitations (mainly the narrowness of the hull) prevented its being upgunned further and considerable redesign was necessary to turn it into a vehicle capable of carrying the very desirable 17pdr gun armament.

All the A24/A27 series were structurally similar, with a hull and turret of simple box shape and composite construction – an inner skin with an outer layer of armour bolted on. Driver and co-driver/hull machine gunner sat in the forward compartment, and the turret crew consisted of the commander, gunner and loader (who was also the radio operator). Tracks were manganese with centre guides, and the engine and transmission were at the rear. Numerous detail modifications were incorporated during the Cromwell's production run, which ended in 1945. Most important innovation was the introduction of all-welded construction in place of rivetting on later models, thus further simplifying mass-production. The Cromwell IV was the definitive production model, built in the largest numbers.

The Challenger

Reverses in the great tank engagements against the Afrika Korps in the Western Desert in 1941 led the British General Staff to ask the Tank Board to investigate the feasibility of mounting a heavy high velocity gun (able to knock out any known German AFV) in British infantry

The Challenger represented the attempt to fit a 17pdr gun to the Cromwell type hull, but needed extensive changes. Though used in limited numbers, the Sherman with 17pdr (Firefly) replaced it for general service. The extra pair of road wheels and the very high turret should be noted.

and cruiser tanks. For the infantry tank requirement it was proposed to fit a 3 in AA gun in a limited traverse mount in the Churchill chassis, though ultimately this idea was abandoned. The 17pdr gun was then in the development stage, and for the cruiser tank requirement the possibility of mounting this weapon in the A27 series was considered. However, the A27 chassis was too narrow to take a turret to hold the 17pdr, so Birmingham Carriage and Wagon, then the A27 design 'parents', evolved a design based closely on the A27, but with a lengthened hull, an extra bogie wheel each side to compensate for the extra weight, and a widened centre hull section. Work on three pilot models was under way by May 1942, and the first was delivered for trials the following August. The A30, as the new vehicle was designated, was based as nearly as possible on Cromwell components. Mechanically it was almost identical, and it had the same Rolls-Royce Meteor engine. The turret to hold the 17pdr gun was designed and built by Stothert and Pitt.

Trials with the prototype showed up several deficiencies; the extra weight, 3 tons more than the Cromwell, led to suspension trouble; there was heavy trunnion loading and slow turret traverse. To overcome the latter defect, electric Metadyne type traverse gear was subsequently installed. The size of 17pdr AP rounds, plus the size of the turret and breech, severely restricted ammunition stowage, and the hull machine gun position was eliminated to provide more room. A further modification found necessary was the reduction of the armour thickness to reduce weight and so improve performance. In January 1943, the prototype trials were assessed to see if a production order was justified. By this time the PzKw IV with 'long' 75mm gun had appeared (and the Tiger was soon to follow) and the fact that the A30 design was a quick way of

getting a tank with 17pdr gun into service swung the balance in favour of its adoption. An order for 200 vehicles was placed, these to be distributed to armoured divisions in similar proportions to AA and close support tanks. This would mean that divisional commanders would have available a tank capable of taking on vehicles with 75mm and 88mm guns on almost equal terms, as far as fire power was concerned. In view of the adverse qualities revealed by the trials, however, it was decided to investigate the possibility of mounting the 17pdr in the M4 Sherman (by then widely used by the British) as a safeguard against failure of the A30 programme.

Numerous troubles were experienced in getting the A30, now named Challenger, into production. It was not until March 1944 that the first production vehicles were ready, by which time it was realized that no provision for water-proofing for deep wading existed. This was essential for getting ashore from LCTs for the forthcoming Overlord landings (June 6, 1944). Meanwhile the Sherman with the 17pdr – known as the Firefly – was available and it was adopted in place of the Challenger. Later in 1944, however, some Challengers were issued to the reconnaissance regiments of British armoured divisions in NW Europe to stiffen the fire power of the 75mm armed Cromwells which were their main equipment.

Birmingham Carriage and Wagon were the original design and production 'parents' for the A27 (Centaur/Cromwell) series, although production delays and difficulties in correcting mechanical deficiencies led to the parentage being transferred to Leyland in May 1943. When Leyland took over the A27, they immediately began work on designing an improved version incorporating modifications to overcome the limitations of the A27 design. Mechanically and dimensionally the improved vehicle, designated A34, was similar to the A27. To avoid the need for widening the hull, as had been necessary in the A30 to take the 17pdr gun, Vickers-Armstrong designed a new 'compact' version of the 17pdr with a shorter barrel, shorter breech, and lighter weight. Known originally as the Vickers HV 75mm (HV: High Velocity), but later called the 77mm gun, it had a performance and penetrating power only slightly inferior to the 17pdr gun and fired the same ammunition. It was intended that the 77mm gun would fit the original A27 type turret with only small modifications, but in the event an enlarged turret was found necessary. The A34 pilot model was ready for tests in February 1944, and among modifications incorporated as a result of trials was a stronger suspension with the addition of track return rollers. By this time the A34 represented a 60 per cent re-design of the A27 and was virtually a new tank. Production deliveries commenced in September 1944, a few vehicles were issued in December 1944 and the A34s, then named Comet, were issued to battalions of 11th Armoured Division after the Rhine crossing in March 1945.

The Comet proved a fast and reliable tank, the first British AFV to come near matching the German Panther in performance and gun power. However, it appeared too late to play any prominent part in British tank combat in the Second World War. Comets subsequently equipped British armoured units after the war and some remained in service until the early 1960s. Like the later marks of Cromwell, the Comet was of all-welded construction.

The Western Desert fighting of 1941–42 had several unrelated chassis designs. This initiated the thinking which led to the Centurion tank. Meanwhile the old weight and dimension limitations to conform with British rail loading gauge had been lifted by the War Office, under pressure from the Department of Tank Design, which was thus able to undertake initial design studies on this basis. At this period, however, the Government had banned development work on projects which could not be in service by 1944 (this was to concentrate work on perfecting existing designs) and authority to proceed was not given until July 1943. AEC were appointed production 'parents' and the new vehicle, designated A41, was to be produced in the first instance for the 'heavy cruiser' role. It was required to mount the largest calibre tank gun (the 17pdr), have a sloped instead of vertical

a profound effect on subsequent British tank policy; in particular the desert fighting finally shattered the old tank versus tank (i.e. 'comparable class') theory and showed that tanks were just as likely to have to support infantry or attack anti-tank guns with HE fire as to engage other tanks. The American M3 medium tank, which was issued to the British in the desert in 1942, effectively fulfilled the need for an AFV which could fire either AP (Armour Piercing) or HE (High Explosive) shot as required. Largely resulting from the desert war tank combats, the War Office revised its policy for future tank development in September 1942 and called for an 'all-purpose' or 'universal' tank chassis which could be developed to fulfil the various roles previously carried out by

glacis to improve frontal protection, and be sufficiently armoured to withstand the German 88mm gun. Road speed was less important than cross-country performance, which had to at least match that of the Comet.

A mock-up of the design was ready by May 1944 and featured modified Horstmann suspension in place of the Christie type of previous cruiser tanks. This was because increasing weight had now exceeded the effectiveness of the Christie suspension. The hull gunner's position was omitted to increase ammunition stowage, and the hull was boat-shaped to improve resistance to mine explosions. The Meteor engine was again used in this vehicle, together with a Morris 8hp auxiliary motor to charge the dynamo and work the fans. A Merrit-Brown

Comet was the successor to Cromwell; it featured a 77mm gun, essentially a 17pdr modified to fit the turret. Note the return rollers introduced to the suspension.

gearbox was standard in this vehicle.

Twenty pilot models were ordered, 15 with 17pdr guns (the last 5 with 77mm guns), and with various combinations of Polsten cannon and Besa machine gun as secondary armament. Pilot models 1–10 had Polstens and rear turret escape doors; pilots 11–15 had Besa MGs instead of Polstens; pilots 16–18 had an additional Besa MG in a ball mount in place of the rear turret escape door; and pilots 19–20 had provision for mounting a Besa MG in the hull front, reverting to the escape door in the turret rear. The last five vehicles had 'Powerflow' gearboxes and were designated A41S. The first six vehicles produced, later called Centurion I, were delivered in May 1945 and rushed to Germany for testing in combat conditions with

Top Centurion Mk I had a 17pdr gun and a 20mm Polsten cannon in the turret. This was the first prototype in April 1945.

Above The Centurion first earned fame in Korea; here Mk IIIs of the 8th Hussars waiting to cross the Imjim River by pontoon bridge in June 1951.

Right The Centurion was the backbone of Britain's armoured forces for over twenty years. Shown here is a Centurion Mk 5 with 20pdr gun in Germany in 1963.

112

22nd Armoured Brigade. However, hostilities had ceased by the time they arrived. Meanwhile in January 1945, an up-armoured vehicle, designated A41A, Centurion II, was produced as a prototype, also armed with a 17pdr gun. This vehicle had a new cast turret and numerous detail improvements. A further projected version was to have a 95 mm howitzer for the close support role, but this was never built.

Ironically, while the Centurion tank was too late to take part in the war for which it was intended, it became one of the most successful tanks of all time, arguably the finest tank in the world in the 1950s and 1960s and still a potent and widely used weapon in the 1970s. Like the T-34, it had the optimum balance of firepower, armour, performance, and reliability, which made it more than a match for almost any other tank in the world. It epitomized what became known as the 'main battle tank', in effect the merging of the two main types of the Second World War – medium tanks and heavy tanks – into a single class with the speed of the mediums and the firepower of the heavy tanks.

The Centurion in its Mk 3 form with 20pdr gun made its name in the Korean War. Not only did it show remarkable agility over the steep terrain – American tanks could not match it – but it was also deadly accurate and almost unstoppable by the enemy. The Mk 5 was in service in the mid 1950s and was produced – and exported – in large numbers. The Mk 7 introduced extra built-in fuel tanks and a much greater range, while the Mk 8 had improved fire control equipment. With the Mk 9 came the introduction of improved armament, a 105 mm gun of excellent performance which subsequently became the 'standard' piece for Western main battle tanks, equipping the American M60, the German Leopard, and the French AMX 30. Kept well up to date with such later developments as infra-red night sights and a ranging machine gun of great effectiveness, the Centurion proved its fighting qualities time and again in the 'little wars' of the 1960s and 1970s. In the Indo–Pakistan War of 1965, and the Arab–Israeli wars of 1967 and 1973, Centurions dominated tank actions and proved superior to both Russian and American made tanks.

A complete 'family' of specialized variants was also developed – bridgelayer, recovery vehicle, beach recovery vehicle (for amphibious operations), an AVRE, and others. Centurions were supplied to Canada, Sweden, Israel, Jordan, Switzerland, Iraq, Denmark, South Africa, Holland, and Australia. In the British Army the Centurion was replaced by the more complicated and sophisticated Chieftain, but with wide export sales and first-class cost-effectiveness the Centurion looks set to soldier on into the 1980s.

Above Centurion Bridge-layer demonstrates the positioning of its bridge; this was one of several variants for special purposes on the Centurion chassis.

Left Centurion AVRE (Armoured Vehicle Royal Engineers) with 165 mm demolition gun, dozer blade, and fascine cradle.

Below Engine change for a Centurion Mk 5 up country in Aden, March 1962. The turret stowage boxes have been removed to give clearance for the engine covers.

First produced in 1945, the Centurion proved to be one of the most successful and reliable tank designs of all time and was still in wide service (in improved form) over 30 years after its introduction. Major users of the Centurion are the Israelis, and the vehicles shown here all have the powerful British-developed 105 mm gun and are Mk 5 and Mk 8 production models retrospectively fitted with this gun. The side skirts protecting the track are removable.

The Sherman tank goes into action for the first time at the Battle of Alamein in October 1942; these are M4A1s, cast hull models, designated Sherman Mk II by the British.

Between the two world wars no great nation made less progress with the development of the tank than the United States. Germany, Russia, and even France, all built up considerable armoured forces in the 1930s, while Britain was rich in ideas for tank warfare if not in material. America had entered the First World War late, however, and the Armistice of November 1918 put an end to the expansion of her promising Tank Corps long before it could be established on its planned war footing. There was thus all too little time for any senior American officers to become versed or experienced in tank warfare, and hardly anyone, other than the tank men, raised a whimper when the US War Department abolished the Tank Corps in 1919. In 1920 the National Defense Act made tanks an Infantry responsibility which virtually relegated tanks and tank development to the lowest priority in the meagre defence budgets of America's lean years. It was not until the German invasion of France and Flanders in May 1940 that impetus was given to the production of big tanks on a large scale and the result was the immortal M3 Medium Tank, variously remembered as the Grant and Lee, which went from drawing board to battlefield in under two years and played a major part in restoring Allied fortunes when at their lowest ebb in the Western Desert fighting.

Between the Wars

The origins of medium tank development in the US Army date back to 1919, just before the abolition of the Tank Corps. To plan for future tank development the Chief of the Tank Corps asked one of his staff officers, Major R.E. Carlson, to make a study of future requirements and prepare a paper on the subject. Carlson had been a member of the Anglo-American Tank Commission, which was responsible for the development of the Mk VIII tank, so he was well placed to be familiar with British ideas on the future of tanks. Carlson's 'Paper on the Development of Tanks' suggested that light tanks in the five ton class and medium tanks in the 20–30 ton class should be produced in future, the latter with a 6pdr (57mm) gun and machine gun armament. These requirements were passed to the Ordnance Department's Rock Island Arsenal which accordingly produced a prototype medium tank, the M1921, to meet the ideas formulated by Carlson. An improved model, the M1922, subsequently produced, was similar but was based in shape much more on the Medium D tank, a somewhat advanced but short-lived British design, and superficially the two had a family resemblance. With a speed of 12mph, the M1922 was half as fast again as the M1921.

By this time, however, the Tank Corps had long been abolished as a separate arm, but in 1921 the Infantry and Ordnance Department had asked the General Staff to approve a future policy for tank development based on Carlson's original paper. After much deliberation, in April 1922 the General Staff did at last make a formal decision and published an outline directive. This document started with the statement:

'The primary mission of the tank is to facilitate the uninterrupted advance of the rifleman in the attack. Its size, armament, speed, and all accessories...must be approached with the above mission as the final objective....'

While this decisively established a definite (if also conservative) policy based on the earliest ideas for the employment of tanks, the rest of the paper went on to water down Major Carlson's original ideas very considerably. The

The American Medium Tanks

entire emphasis was on saving money and resources even if this meant sacrificing technical and tactical progress at the same time. The two classes of tanks commended by Carlson were retained, the light tank and the medium tank, but the medium tank was not now to exceed 15 tons, the weight limit of existing Engineer Corps bridging equipment. Speeds of medium tanks were not to exceed 12 mph, machine guns were to be arranged to enfilade enemy trenches as the vehicles crossed, and a heavier calibre gun was to be carried to engage enemy tanks. Two particular statements emphasize the financial stringency of the period:

'...for the present funds and effort will be applied principally to development purposes rather than to the construction of complete tank units;' and 'Expenditure of funds on existing tanks will be limited to the amount necessary to keep those in actual service in repair and those in storage from deterioration.'

As a result of the General Staff's ruling, the M1921 and M1922 prototypes were outside the new 15 ton limit so these were held in abeyance and work started on other designs. In 1926 the General Staff allowed another 23 ton vehicle (the T1) to be made but concentration on 15 ton types continued. Efforts were diverted to a few Christie vehicles of about 13 tons weight which were, of course, 'commercial' designs, while, by 1930, the Ordnance Department had developed the T2 Medium tank which was designed to the 15 ton limit and was based in shape and layout on the British Medium Mk II. The T3 and T4 vehicles which followed this were Christie designs once again. Until the T4 all these tanks had existed as prototypes only but in 1935 16 of the Christie T4 Medium tanks were built at Rock Island, the first medium tanks

(as opposed to light tanks) to be built in quantity since 1919. Between 1920 and 1935 only 35 tanks of all kinds were built in America, and American tank forces were smaller than those of any other major nation.

The next type of medium tank was designed by Rock Island Arsenal in 1937/38 on more conventional lines. Designated T5, this new vehicle conformed almost completely to the General Staff's original 1922 outline for medium tanks. It was within the 15 tons weight limit – at least on paper, for this was exceeded very early on in development – it had an all-round machine gun armament and even featured angled plates on the rear fenders so that bullets could be deflected down into the trenches as the vehicle crossed. The main armament was a 37mm gun, matching the calibre of most contemporary foreign tanks, and for economy and standardization as many components and features as possible were utilized from the existing M2 light tank which was then also in production. Among these features were the same Continental 7-cylinder 250 bhp engine, vertical volute suspension, sprockets, similar track, and similar transmission. The Continental engine was a radial air-cooled unit adapted from an aero engine. This had been adopted in the design of the light tanks to avoid expenditure on developing new highpower motors for tanks, another direct result of the economic stringency of the times.

The T5 prototype was completed at Rock Island Arsenal in 1938. With its eight machine guns – two firing forward, four in the barbette, and two on the turret sides – plus its 25 mm armour it exactly fitted the official General Staff conception of a tank for infantry support. Tests of the vehicle showed it to be under-powered, however, and it was decided that a bigger

Left and top Centurion
Mk V, re-armed with a
105 mm gun, and in
service with the Israeli
Defence Force.
Above An Israeli
Centurion ARV.

engine was necessary. One proposal was to fit a diesel motor, and an alternative was to fit a larger Wright Continental engine, the 9-cylinder R975 350bhp unit. In this revised form the prototype was actually rebuilt, being then designated T5 Phase III. Trials of the modified vehicle were completed in early 1939 and the design was standardized as the M2 Medium Tank.

Bristling with machine guns, the Medium Tank M2A1 of 1940 reflected the 'infantry support' ideas of the First World War. Note in particular the guns behind the barbette which are arranged to fire on to deflector plates at the rear of the hull.

With the new engine and other detail changes, including wider tracks, the weight had crept up to 19 tons but by this time bridging limits had, in any case, been raised. A production order for 15 M2 Mediums was given to Rock Island Arsenal in August 1939 and, with the addition of two more development vehicles, the total M2 output amounted to 18 vehicles. At the time of the German invasion of France in May 1940 these were the only up-to-date medium tanks in the US Army. It is interesting to compare this paltry figure with later production – over 40,000 medium tanks were built in the war period ahead. By the time the first M2s were in production war had started in Europe and work was put in hand to produce an improved model. This was designated Medium Tank M2A1. Compared to the original M2 it had an uprated (400bhp) supercharged engine, armour maximum increased from 25 mm to 32 mm, strengthened bogie units, slightly wider tracks, splash rails added on the glacis plate, and an enlarged turret. These changes increased the overall combat weight to just over 23 tons.

Experimental work carried out with the original T5/M2 vehicles included the installation of a Guiberson diesel engine and twin 37 mm guns in one vehicle (T5E1) and the conversion of the original T5 Phase III vehicle to an experimental self-propelled carriage. In this guide it was designated T5E2, being converted between March and May 1939 to mount a standard 75 mm pack howitzer in its suitably modified hull front. The turret was removed and a new small offset turret was fitted which held an optical rangefinder for the howitzer. This conversion was merely an idea by the Ordnance Department to test the feasibility of producing a self-propelled gun on the medium tank chassis should such a vehicle be required in future. In the event, the T5E2 was to become the vital design on which the M3 Medium Tank was later based, and from which, in turn, the M4 Sherman was developed.

The Medium Tank Programme

When Germany invaded Poland in September 1939 the US Army possessed no modern medium tanks and only a few new light tanks. No facilities for producing tanks on a large scale existed at all. Rock Island Arsenal had built most of the tanks produced in the 1920s and 1930s, but was primarily an artillery plant and there was no space for large tank production lines. Plans existed, however, to place contracts with heavy engineering firms and locomotive builders should the need for tanks in quantity arise, the view being that this sort of firm would be adept at the heavy casting and assembly work involved in tank production. Accordingly the first big contract, for M2A4 light tanks, went to one such firm, American Car & Foundry, in October 1939 on the basis of competitive tendering. 'Educational' orders went at the same time to two other heavy engineering plants, Van Dorn and Baldwin, again for light tanks. In the fall of 1939 the improved medium tank design, the M2A1, was still being worked out and the 'Phoney War' in Europe gave valuable breathing space.

In May 1940 the M2A1 was ready. Almost simultaneously the German panzers were sweeping all before them in the advance into France and Belgium, and America's grave shortage of tanks suddenly became a cause for political concern. In the Senate, Henry Cabot Lodge, who has just witnessed military manoeuvres in Louisiana said: 'I have recently seen all the tanks in the United States, about 400 in number,[1] or about one finger of the fanlike German advance about which we have read, or about the number destroyed in two days of fighting in the current European War. The Germans have a rough total of 3000'.

Criticism from press, public, and politicians alike at America's general unpreparedness for war led to the introduction of the National Munitions Program on June 30, 1940, by which time France had capitulated and Britain was al-

[1] All but about 25 were M2 light tanks or M1 combat cars, suitable only for scouting or armed reconnaissance.

most defenceless and seemingly about to be invaded herself. The plan covered all aspects of defence, of course, but included a requirement for 1741 medium tanks to be produced in the next 18 months. On July 10, 1940, a new Armored Force was formed under General Adna R.Chaffee, to take over all responsibility for tanks from the existing infantry and cavalry commands. The scene was now set for an expansion of America's tank forces on a dramatic and impressive scale.

The Ordnance Department had earmarked American Locomotive Co. and Baldwin Locomotive Co. as possible builders of medium tanks since these firms had spare capacity for the task. However, such plans were soon revised. Early in June a National Defense Advisory Commission had been formed to help prepare the new Munitions Program and among its members, one of several leaders of industry, was William S.Knudsen, President of General Motors, whose special task was to advise on matters concerning mechanized equipment. Knudsen considered that tanks on the vast scale now required could not be produced quickly enough by heavy engineering plants. He argued that such firms were mainly used to small 'bespoke' orders for locomotives, cranes and the like which did not necessarily give them the necessary expertize for turning out tanks by the hundred.[2] He maintained that the answer to the tank production problem was to harness the resources of the mighty Detroit automobile industry and suggested that a purpose-built plant should be erected at Detroit specially to build the new medium tanks which were required. Existing automobile factories could not be used because the production plant needed was different and these factories were in any case required for other military production like trucks and engines.

The Ordnance Department agreed that such a scheme would be worth investigating, if only because the need for additional tank production facilities was most urgent. Knudsen contacted the President of Chrysler Corporation, K.T. Keller, and asked if he would be prepared to undertake the task of setting up a new tank arsenal on behalf of the government, using Chrysler personnel and resources. Keller moved fast and sent a team of engineers to Rock Island Arsenal to look at the M2A1 prototype and bring back a set of drawings – total weight 186 pounds – to the Chrysler plant in Detroit. By June 17 the engineers and production planners started to work on estimating the work force, the size of the plant, the size of the building, costing, and the thousands of other problems involved in turning out tanks, from scratch from a building not yet erected. One of the most complex industrial schemes of all time, the planning and building of what became known as the Detroit Tank Arsenal would have been a major undertaking even in the leisurely days of peace. The Chrysler engineers, however, were asked to have the plant fully operational within a year and turning out 100 tanks a month.

Planning and costing for the entire project took exactly a month, during which time Chrysler engineers built a complete full-size wooden pattern model of a M2A1 using the Rock Island plans; this was to assist in the design of production plant. On July 17, 1940, Chrysler presented the full scheme to the Ordnance Department for approval. Cost of the complete arsenal was estimated at $21 million with a proposed output of ten tanks per day at $30000 each less armament. The formal contract was signed on August 15 and covered building of the arsenal and production of 1000 M2A1 Medium tanks. These immediate plans were soon to change, however.

The 75 mm Gun

On June 5, 1940, just as Knudsen was pushing his ideas for a special tank arsenal, the Chief of Infantry – then still responsible for tank forces – forwarded a report on future requirements to the Ordnance Department. Based on staff studies of the tank fighting in the French campaign just ending, it had been noted that the Germans had been using tanks with 75 mm guns (on some models of the PzKpfw IV). The Chief of Infantry urged that any future medium tanks produced should be armed with guns of at least this calibre. In short, tanks like the M2 and M2A1 with their 37 mm guns had been outmoded almost overnight.

A few days after the thousand M2A1 tanks had been ordered, the new Chief of the Armored Force, Chaffee, met senior Ordnance Department officers at Aberdeen Proving Ground for a conference on future tank requirements. It was agreed here that the provision of a tank with a 75 mm gun was now of paramount importance. However, studies by the Ordnance Department showed conclusively that a weapon of this large calibre could not be mounted in the turret of the existing M2A1. An entirely new larger turret would be needed which would impose delays since no turret of the size required had ever previously been built in America and much work would be needed on such a project to overcome the necessary design and casting problems.

It was decided that while such work should be put in hand at once, the need for a tank with a 75 mm gun could be met by mounting the weapon in the hull, as had been tried successfully in the experimental T5E2 the previous year.

[2] The heavy engineering firms engaged in tank production, however, disproved this theory very quickly with an excellent war output record.

One of the generation of main battle tanks in service in the 1970s, Britain's Chieftain shows the typical low profile, 'inverted frying pan' turret, and large calibre gun. Commander and gunner are shown (*below*) inside the vehicle, the commander seated beneath his cupola.

Pilot model of the
Medium Tank M3 on
trials; the M2 parentage is
obvious by comparison
with the illustration on
page 120.

This would enable most of the basic features of the M2A1 to be utilized, including the complete chassis virtually unaltered and the same engine and mechanical parts. Only the hull and super-structure would need revision and this was to be based on that of the T5E2 as far as possible. The turret with 37mm gun was to be retained, however, and would be offset to the left on the hull top in place of the rangefinder turret in the T5E2. Thus was born the M3 Medium Tank, recognized from the start as an interim design while work continued on a medium tank with 75mm gun in a fully travers-ing turret – the design which was later to be-come the M4 Medium tank, better known as the Sherman.

On August 28, shortly after the Aberdeen decision, the contract for the thousand M2A1s was cancelled in favour of an identical contract for 1000 M3s. At this time the M3 had still not been designed, but the Ordnance Department gave themselves 60 days to achieve this, during which time it was estimated that 10000 working drawings would be necessary. Meanwhile, con-struction of the arsenal was to proceed even though the changed plans meant that some of the plant would have to be further altered or even replaced for the new design.

Building of Detroit Arsenal started early in September 1940 on a 100-acre site just outside Detroit. The skeleton of the building, 1380ft long and 500ft wide, was completed by January 1941 and most of the construction work had been finished by March. Meanwhile Chrysler engineers were designing plant piecemeal as the M3 drawings were completed in stages at Aber-deen.

As well as designing the vehicle itself the necessary 75mm gun had to be designed. This work was carried out by the Watervliet Arsenal which based the design on the famous French 75mm gun, adopted as a standard field gun by the US Army in 1918. In mid-July an initial 'off the drawing board' order for 1308 guns and mountings was placed and the first were delivered in April 1941 just in time to go into the M3 pilot models. The first version, designated M2 had a barrel 84in long and had a muzzle velocity of 1860fps. A later improved model, the M3, had a longer 110in barrel and increased muzzle velocity of 2300fps. Most M3 Mediums were fitted with the shorter M2 gun, but the M3 gun was being produced in time for fitting in later production vehicles.

Planned for fitting in the M3 Medium (and M3 Light) tanks was a gyrostabilizer, a revolutionary innovation in a tank. Based on a principle long used in naval gunnery, the idea of the gyrostabilizer was to maintain the gun at any given elevation irrespective of the pitching of the vehicle as it moved across country. Previously a tank could only fire with any certainty of accuracy when stationary. With a gyrostabilizer a tank could fire with accuracy while on the move, a facility which gave a definite tactical advantage. Even so subsequent experience was to show that less than full use was made of the gyrostabilizer. The gyrostabilizer was based on the well-known gyroscope principle and in essence it consisted of a gyro attached to the gun cradle on the same axis and set spinning. Any subsequent displacement due to vertical movement of the vehicle caused the gyro, and hence the gun barrel, to return to its original axis. For use in tanks the gyrostabilizer system had to be reduced in size to fit a confined space and be tough enough to survive the severe combat conditions in which tanks are expected to operate. From July 1941 the gyrostabilizer was fitted to both the 75mm and 37mm guns of the M3 Medium tanks. Some early vehicles were produced without stabilizers but in many cases they were retrospectively fitted. When the longer M3 gun appeared, it was necessary to provide different settings for the stabilizer to take account of the longer, heavier barrel. Subsequently most vehicles with the earlier guns were fitted with counterweights on the muzzles so that they simulated the weight of the M3 barrel and could be used with identical stabilizer settings, thus simplifying maintenance.

M3 Production

The speed at which the M3 was designed gave rise to immense problems. Difficulties multiplied when plant delivery fell behind or outside contractors for small components could not keep up with the development timetable. For the first couple of months of production most of the M3s turned out from Detroit were almost literally hand-made, in part since essential machinery did not arrive or was found to be unsuitable for use on arrival. The earliest M3s delivered sometimes lacked either the 75mm or the 37mm gun, and sometimes both, but they were better than nothing at all for crew training. More literally than most tanks, the M3 Medium was built straight 'off the drawing board'. Final design work was not completed until March 1941 and the pilot models were produced less than three weeks later in early April 1941.

In addition to production at Detroit Arsenal it was decided in October 1940 to order M3s from two of the big engineering firms as originally planned. Hence American Locomotive Co. and Baldwin Locomotive Works were brought in and sent their engineers to work with the Chrysler engineers on production planning. In the event American Locomotive and Baldwin completed their pilot models a little ahead of Detroit Arsenal – mainly because they were not involved in building a factory at the same time. The severe shortage of components in these early days is reflected in the fact that when American Locomotive completed their M3 pilot model in the first week of April 1941 there existed only one complete set of transmissions and final drive, freshly turned out by the con-

M3 Medium Tanks in production at the Detroit Tank Arsenal, April 1942. These early vehicles have ports for fixed machine guns in the hull front, a feature soon discarded.

9

10

11

12

13

14

15

10

16

17

18

19

20

21

22

23

24

25

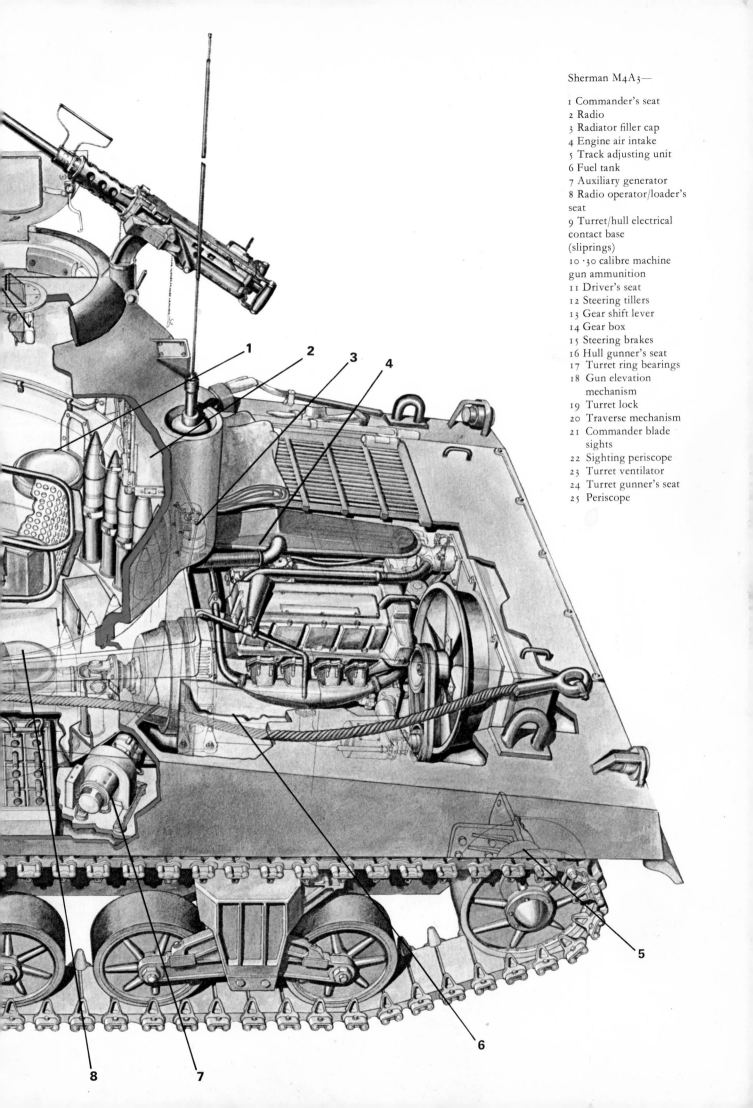

Sherman M4A3—

1 Commander's seat
2 Radio
3 Radiator filler cap
4 Engine air intake
5 Track adjusting unit
6 Fuel tank
7 Auxiliary generator
8 Radio operator/loader's seat
9 Turret/hull electrical contact base (sliprings)
10 ·30 calibre machine gun ammunition
11 Driver's seat
12 Steering tillers
13 Gear shift lever
14 Gear box
15 Steering brakes
16 Hull gunner's seat
17 Turret ring bearings
18 Gun elevation mechanism
19 Turret lock
20 Traverse mechanism
21 Commander blade sights
22 Sighting periscope
23 Turret ventilator
24 Turret gunner's seat
25 Periscope

M3 Medium Tank in service with the US Army, July 1942, soon after delivery. This vehicle has the short M2 75 mm gun with a counterweight on the muzzle to balance the gyrostabilizer which was set for the longer M3 75 mm gun.

tractors for this vital part of the vehicle. This was installed in American Locomotive's pilot model so that it could make a ceremonial drive past at the factory for the Secretary of War and the General Staff. Immediately after this the same transmission was unshipped from the vehicle and rushed to the Baldwin plant so that it could be fitted in their pilot model for a similar ceremony a few days later. The last pilot model completed was by Detroit Arsenal on April 11, 1941 and this vehicle was ceremonially presented to the Chief of Ordnance on April 24 together with the first actual production vehicle which had been paid for by subscription from Chrysler dealers throughout America.

Meanwhile although the M2A1 had been displaced from the Detroit Arsenal scheme, it was nonetheless built in small numbers. Rock Island Arsenal undertook production and turned out 94 (of 106 ordered) between November 1940 and August 1941. The decision was taken to build these as an interim type to have available while the M3 reached production status. These vehicles were used only for training and experimental work in the United States, however, and saw no combat service.

The British Involvement

The withdrawal through Dunkirk in May 1940 left the British Army with only about 150 tanks, mostly obsolete, for home defence against an invasion which could be expected hourly. The need for tanks was desperate and a British Tank Mission was sent to America in June 1940 with the specific task of arranging direct contracts with American firms to build tanks for Britain. With considerable optimism the British Mission's original idea was to have tanks built in America to existing British designs. However,

Knudsen of the National Defense Advisory Commission pointed out to the US Government that to allow this dispersion of effort at a time when America was also desperately short of tanks would be a waste of existing resources.

The British Mission was told that it had to accept American designs or nothing. At the time there were, of course, only two available designs in the pipeline, the M3 Medium and M3 Light. Britain took both types on a 'cash and carry' basis (this was before the days of Lend-Lease). In October 1940, however, Britain placed contracts with Baldwin, Lima Locomotive Works, and Pullman-Standard Car Co. for M3s modified slightly to suit them better for British requirements. The main change requested was a new, lower turret which accommodated British radio equipment (rather than in the hull which was American practice at that time). The prominent machine gun cupola of the original M3 was eliminated since by British standards the vehicle was considered too high. Design of the turret for British requirements was completed by the Ordnance Department in November 1940 and a test installation was made in one of the M2 tanks. The British version of the M3 was later called the Grant (after General Grant) and deliveries of these vehicles were rushed to North Africa early in 1942 where they were first in action at the big Gazala battle in May 1942. The Grant's appearance at this time had a profound effect on Britain's fortunes in the desert fighting. For the first time the British tank forces had an accurate high velocity gun of a calibre powerful enough to match the best German guns and at the same time able to give indirect support fire with HE, a facility lacking in all previous tanks in British service.

The Lend-Lease Act was passed in March

1941 and this made further vehicles available to Britain which did not have to be paid for in cash. Accordingly the British also received the standard version of the M3 Medium, which they called the Lee. By October 1942, at the time of the Second Battle of Alamein, there were nearly 600 M3s of both types in British service (not all of them were in Egypt). With the M4 Shermans which were just arriving, Grants and Lees formed the backbone of the British tank forces for the Alamein battle. Earlier in 1942 a depot had been set up in the desert near Cairo where American personnel trained British crews on their new vehicles. Further M3s were sent to Britain for training purposes.

Later when the M4 replaced the M3 in British service in the Western Desert the redundant Grants and Lees were shipped to Australia for use in the campaigns against the Japanese. With a less critical need for modern equipment in the

each side, with a rear idler and sprockets at the front. The Wright Continental R975 nine-cylinder air-cooled radial engine was at the rear with access doors for maintenance in the hull back plate. Fuel tanks flanked each side of the engine compartment. The drive shaft led forward under the floor of the fighting compartment to the gearbox which was sited alongside the driver who sat at the left front of the vehicle. The driver also operated twin machine guns in the nose (these were sometimes removed from later vehicles). Access to the transmission for maintenance purposes was from outside the vehicle, by a three-piece cast nose housing which was secured by bolts. The remainder of the hull was made of face-hardened plates, and riveted construction was used throughout (except for some subsequent production models noted later). Armour maximum was 2 in (50 mm) on the upper hull front and turret. Sides and

Far East, the M3s were used by the British and Australian regiments fighting in Burma and the South West Pacific until the end of the war, though long replaced elsewhere by Sherman tanks. The Canadian Army was another major user of the M3, both Grants and Lees.

In late 1940 the Canadian Government ordered 1157 M3s which were to be built by Montreal Locomotive Works, a subsidiary of American Locomotive Co. These Canadian vehicles had small detail changes, the main one being the provision of mud chutes between the bogies primarily to clear snow and slush in the winter training conditions which were experienced in Canada.

Anatomy of the M3

The chassis of the M3 Medium tank was essentially similar to that of the M2 and M2A1 which preceded it. Suspension consisted of three vertical volute bogies of the standard design

front lower hull were 1½ in thick. The turret mounted a 37 mm M5 or M6 gun with a co-axial ·30 calibre machine gun. Turret ring was 5 ft in diameter and could be traversed by hand or hydraulically. In the American M3 (the Lee) the cupola normally rotated with the turret, but it could also be rotated independently by hand if desired. A further ·30 calibre machine gun could be mounted in the cupola, but this was frequently removed. The British M3 (the Grant) lacked a cupola but had an extended rear bustle which housed the radio equipment.

The roomy fighting compartment was dominated by the 75 mm gun in a barbette which had a limited traverse of 15 degrees each side and had elevation limits (−9° to +20°). This gun was both the M3's strength and also its weakness in tactical terms. While it provided at the time a bigger punch than any previous Allied tank, to bring the gun into action meant exposing the vehicle's high silhouette, which in the Western

A troop of M3 Medium Tanks (Lee Mk I to the British) equipping the famous Canadian regiment, The Fort Garry Horse, based in England in February 1942. These vehicles have the long M3 75 mm gun.

Desert fighting could have severe, and even decisive, consequences. With lack of all-round traverse the vehicle suffered from the same limitations as a self-propelled gun, so that out-flanking by the enemy could only be countered by moving the complete vehicle, which was not always possible. Thus no time was lost in re-placing the M3 once its successor the M4 was available, but in the existing conditions of 1942 the M3 Medium, for all its defects of design, was a most important addition to the British ar-moury.

M3 Production Models

Several changes were made in the design of the M3 series during its production life. Some re-sulted from combat or user experience while others were production expedients.

A particular problem with American tank production in the 1939–45 period was the constant shortage of suitable engines. In the earlier part of the war the policy of using adapted aero engines in tanks presented as many problems as it solved. The fact that suitable engines were available saved production time and cost, but the National Munitions Program of 1940 also called for a vast increase in aircraft production which drastically reduced aero-type engines available for fitting in tanks. The quest for suitable alternative power plants partly led to some of the model changes which followed. The production series for M3 Medium tanks is summarized in chronological order:

M3: Original production type as designed with Wright R975 (Whirlwind) engine and all-riveted construction. Built by American Loco (April 1941–August 1942, 385 vehicles), Bald-win (April 1941–March 1942, 295 vehicles), Detroit Tank Arsenal (April 1941–August 1942, 3243 vehicles), Pressed Steel (July 1941–July 1942, 501 vehicles), Pullman (August 1941–July 1942, 500 vehicles).

M3 (Diesel): A variation on the standard M3, this had a Guiberson diesel motor replacing the Wright gasoline unit to overcome engine short-ages. The British designation for the M3 was Lee Mk I.

M3A1: Identical mechanically to the M3, this version differed in having a cast hull. Built by American Locomotive Co. (February–August 1942, 300 vehicles), as this firm had casting facilities for this type of hull.

M3A1 (Diesel): As for M3A1 but with Guiber-son diesel motor. The British designation for the M3A1 was Lee Mk II.

M3A2: This was similar to the M3 but had a welded instead of a riveted hull. Built by Bald-win (January–February 1942). Only 12 of these were built because the adoption of a new engine led to a designation change.

M3A3: This was simply the all-welded M3A2 fitted with twin General Motors 6–71 diesel motors. Built by Baldwin (March–December 1942, 322 vehicles). The British designation for the M3A2 was Lee Mk III and for the M3A3 it was Lee Mk IV. Lee Mk V was the designation given to a M3A3 re-engined with the Wright R975 unit.

M3A4: This was similar to the original M3 but had the Chrysler A-57 Multibank engine re-placing the Wright engine. The Chrysler A-57 was a makeshift power unit made up of five motor-car engines on a common crankshaft, specially developed for tanks at Detroit Arsenal.

A brand new M3 medium undergoes firing trials on a range close to the Detroit Tank Arsenal before delivery to the Army. One defect of the design is well shown here: firing the 75 mm gun, even hull down, left a high silhouette showing to the enemy.

The M3A4 was built at Detroit only (June–August 1942, 109 vehicles). The chassis on this model was lengthened slightly to take the bulkier engine. The British designation for M3A4 was Lee Mk VI.

M3A5: This was the same as the M3A3 but had a riveted instead of welded hull. It was built by Baldwin (January–November 1942, 591 vehicles). The British designation for this model was Grant Mk II. The original Grant – the basic M3 with the British type turret – then took the designation Grant Mk I.

The sponson side doors weakened the hull sides and it became common practice to weld up these openings in overhauled, or even new, vehicles. In very late production models the doors were eliminated completely. The very last M3 series production vehicles turned out (November–December 1942) had later pattern volute bogies with trailing return rollers of the type used in M4 tanks.

Special Purpose Models

Like all obsolescent vehicles, the M3 Medium chassis was pressed into service from 1943 for several important auxiliary roles. Old vehicles with the guns and turret removed were used as M33 Prime Movers for artillery use pending the development of high-speed tractors. M33s were widely used in the North West Europe campaign towing 155mm and 240mm guns. A couple of flame-throwing devices were developed for the M3 and there were also numerous experimental conversions, used in developing new ideas.

Of major service importance were the tank recovery vehicles (TRV). The US Army developed the T2 TRV (later standardized as the M31) which appeared in several forms depending on the basic chassis. This handy and widely used type had its guns removed and replaced by dummies. A boom was attached and operated by a 60000lb winch housed in the fighting compartment. The turret basket was removed and a big access door took the place of the original 75mm gun mantlet (though it was disguised as a mantlet). Telescopic legs were attached to the boom and could either support it from the rear decking or from the ground for lifting and winching work. The turret and boom were normally traversed aft and the boom was held by a special plate which replaced the original 37mm gun mantlet.

The British produced an ARV (armoured recovery vehicle) of their own, by removing the turret and guns and fitting a winch internally. This vehicle, the Grant ARV I, was equipped to the same standards as other British Mk I ARVs complete with demountable A-frame jib.

An important British conversion was the Grant CDL in which an armoured searchlight turret replaced the original turret. This vehicle, replacing the Matilda CDL, equipped a whole brigade – CDL was an abbreviation for 'Canal Defence Light', a quite meaningless title intended to confuse the inquisitive and suggesting a role as an illuminator of defences. In fact, the equipment was intended to facilitate night attacks. But Grant CDLs were never used, except in small numbers for the Rhine and Elbe crossings in 1945. The US Army was impressed by the CDL and built more than 300 of these themselves by converting redundant vehicles to equip six battalions. Known under the 'camouflage' designation of T10 Shop Tractors, they were never used.

The British converted Grants as Scorpions for mine clearing with flail rotors. These saw limited use in Tunisia and the invasion of Sicily and Italy but they played an important part in the development of the more famous Sherman Crab which was widely used in the D-Day landings in 1944. One of the first American mine-clearing devices was developed for the M3. This was the T1 Mine Exploder, a system of trailed and pushed heavy rollers (the idea was transferred to the M4 Medium when this vehicle was standardized).

Two major self-propelled guns (the M7 and M12) were also developed on the M3 chassis. Earlier attempts to make a self-propelled gun version of the M3, however, resulted in the T24 3in Gun Motor Carriage which utilized a redundant AA gun of 1918 vintage on what was virtually an open-topped M3. Developed in September 1941, tests showed it to be far too high and clumsy and the project was dropped in favour of the T40, a modified design with the same 3in gun in a more compact mount set lower in the hull. Trials were promising and the vehicle was standardized as the M9 Gun Motor Carriage on the understanding that at least 50 old 3in guns were available for fitting. However, only 28 guns could subsequently be found and the M9 was never produced, an unusual example of standardization without production following.

The M3 Replaced

M4 Medium tank production started in July 1942 and by the end of that year was in full swing. As rapidly as possible the plants building M3s switched over to M4s and the last M3s left the production lines in December 1942. The eclipse of the M3 in US service was rapid. M3s first entered US Army service in late summer 1941, but when the M4 was standardized in October 1941, the M3 was reclassified 'substitute standard' and was further reclassified

One of the first self-propelled guns to see wide Allied service was M7 105 mm Howitzer Motor Carriage, known to the British as the Priest. Originally built on the M3 medium chassis (as here), later models were on the M4 medium chassis. Priest first saw action with the British in the Western Desert in 1942.

'limited standard' in April 1943. In April 1944 the M3 was declared obsolete by the US Army and by this time was almost out of service, even for training. Special purpose variants, particularly the M31 TRV remained in use until after the end of the war. M3s saw little actual combat service with the US Army although some were used in the Torch landings in November 1942, and they were widely used by US armoured divisions in Britain (these M3s were replaced by Shermans for the Normandy landings).

Except for special purpose variants, most British Grant and Lee models were also swiftly withdrawn as soon as the Sherman was available in quantity from the end of 1942 onwards. Most of the 8th Army's Grants and Lees were sent east in early 1943, going to the Australian army for service in the South West Pacific area as a partial replacement for the Matilda. One British regiment, the 3rd Carabineers, was equipped with Grants and Lees (mostly the latter) in Burma 1944–45 where they spearheaded the advance south and were in service until the end of the war.

The Japanese gave very little armour opposition, however, so the M3 was more than adequate for the job it was asked to do, mainly to support the infantry. Ironically enough this was the very function for which the Americans had mainly developed medium tanks in the inter-war years. The jungle fighting against the Japanese was the closest the M3 got to 'facilitating the advance of the rifleman in the attack'. But by 1945 such ideas, like the M3 tanks themselves, were absurdly out of date.

The M4 Medium Tank – The Sherman

Once the design had been completed, the Ordnance Department instantly began work on its replacement. In April 1941 five provisional schemes were shown to the Armored Force, and the simplest was selected for development. Designated Medium Tank T6, this was to have the same chassis and mechanical layout as the M2A1 and M3, a turtle-shaped cast hull, access doors at the side, and a centrally mounted cast turret carrying a 75 mm gun with simple rotary gun sight and a co-axial ·30 calibre machine gun. A cupola was to be mounted on the turret as in the M3 and another feature derived from the M3 was to be twin ·30 calibre machine guns in a fixed mount in the hull front. There was a single hatch for the driver in the hull top above his station. A wooden mock-up with all these characteristics was completed and inspected by the Armored Force Board in May 1941. The Board gave its approval for work to proceed with a prototype vehicle, subject to several changes in detail.

The T6 proper was completed in September 1941 with minor changes which included removal of the cupola. This, and the then novel idea – by US standards – of mounting the radio equipment at the back of the turret instead of inside the hull, stemmed from British influence, via the British Tank Mission which had visited America to purchase tanks for British service. Another British device later incorporated in the design was a 2in smoke mortar mounted in the turret roof.

The T6 was standardized as the Medium Tank M4 in October 1941 after satisfactory conclusion of running trials at Aberdeen Proving Ground, Maryland. Plans were made to put the M4 into production in early 1942 with a phased replacement of the M3 series vehicles on the various assembly lines then in operation. A major design change before production began was the elimination of the side doors which gave a stronger structure and simplified casting. As a substitute a second hatch was fitted in the hull top above the assistant driver's station and a belly escape hatch was added. The cast turtle-shaped hull presented further production problems since casting facilities at the heavy engineering plants would not be able to meet the demand, which at one stage in 1942 was set at a target of 2000 vehicles a month (though this was later scaled down). Accordingly a simpler box-like welded hull was designed which was within the less sophisticated production capabilities of plants without casting facilities or experience. The vehicles with welded hulls were designated M4 and those with cast hulls M4A1.

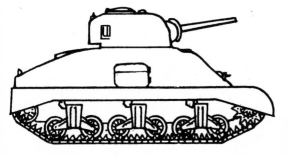

M4A1 'Sherman' 75 mm

Production Arrangements

The M4 series vehicles were built in eleven different plants, and hundreds of outside subcontractors were involved in the supply of components. The M4, or Sherman as it was known to the British, was produced in greater numbers than any American tank before or since and became the standard medium tank produced in the United States armament programme from 1942–44, with production tailing off in 1945. In addition to plants which had been building M3s and in 1942 switched to M4s, the Ford Motor Company, Federal Machine and Welder, Pacific Car and Foundry, and Fisher Body, were all involved in building various models of the M4. A second purpose-built plant to turn out tanks was built (from January 1942) and operated at Grand Blanc, Michigan, by Fisher Body on similar terms to the Chrysler-operated Detroit Tank Arsenal.

As originally designed the M4 had the same engine and chassis as its predecessors, the M2A1 and M3. The Wright-built Continental R-975 engine was basically a de-rated and adapted aero engine, with nine cylinder radial layout and air cooling.

This was a very efficient unit, the original adaptation stemming from the 1930s when it was cheaper to use an existing aero engine than work out a new design specifically for tanks. However, the massive US rearmament scheme of 1940–42 made it quickly apparent that this source of engines would be insufficient to meet demand, particularly as aircraft production had

A diesel-engined Medium Tank M4A2 (British Sherman III) comes ashore during a landing exercise in North Africa for the landing in Sicily.

also been greatly expanded with consequent demand for the same engine. Alternative power units were needed by the time the M3 Medium (Lee) went into production. A few diesel motors were the first used to alleviate the supply problem, but these were not entirely satisfactory and were never used in the M4. Other types of engine were used, however, and these gave rise to the different production models in the M4 series.

M4 Series Models (with Engines and Main Armament)

M4 This was the original design with Continental engine but with the simplified all-welded hull instead of the cast hull initially devised. It was actually the third type to go into production.

Total production was 8389, of which 6748 were fitted with the 75mm gun and 1641 with the 105mm howitzer (see below, Design Improvement).

The British designation for the M4 was Sherman I, while for those with the 105mm the suffix B was added, i.e. Sherman IB. A late production M4 built at Detroit with combination cast/rolled hull front was designated Sherman Hybrid I.

M4A1 Original design based closely on the T6 prototype with cast hull and Continental engine, it was the first type in production.

Total production was 9677, of which 6281 were fitted with the 75mm gun and 3396 with the 76mm gun (see below, Design Improvement).

The British designation for the M4A1 was Sherman II, while for those with the 76mm gun the suffix A was added, i.e. Sherman IIA.

M4A2 This was a vehicle with a welded hull but utilizing the General Motors 6046 diesel engine. This power unit had been produced from January 1941 for the M3A3 medium tank and was adapted for the M4 immediately production was authorized. The unit consisted of two GM truck engines, one each side of the engine compartment, each geared to a common prop shaft. The M4A2 was the second type actually in production, early models following closely after the first M4A1s. The M4A2 was the major type supplied under Lend-Lease to the Russians. Other major users were the British and the US Marines. Few, if any, M4A2s were used by the US Army.

Total production was 11283, of which 8053 were fitted with the 75mm gun and 3230 with the 76mm gun (see below, Design Improvement).

The British designation for the M4A2 was Sherman III, while for those with the 76mm gun the suffix A was added, i.e. Sherman IIIA.

M4A3 A model with welded hull but utilizing

Many M4s were supplied to the Red Army under Lend-Lease arrangements. These diesel-engined M4A2s pass cavalry on the Russian front. Note the all-steel tracks and the extra fuel drums and unditching beams, all typical Soviet features.

the Ford GAA engine, a V-8 unit which was specially developed as a tank engine to replace the Continental. It was authorized for production in January 1942, being developed by Ford on behalf of the Ordnance Department. It subsequently became the new standard tank engine and the M4A3 became the most important model in US service, together with the M4 and M4A1. Other types, with extemporized engines, were thereafter mainly allocated to Lend-Lease supplies. Relatively few M4A3s were supplied to other nations.

Total production was 11424 of which 5015 were fitted with the 75mm gun, 3370 with the 76mm gun, and 3039 with the 105mm howitzer (see below, Design Improvement).

The British designation for the M4A3 was Sherman IV, while for those with the 76mm gun the suffix A was added, i.e. Sherman IVA, and for the few, if any, received with the 105mm the suffix B was added, i.e. Sherman IVB.

M4A3E2 The 5015 M4A3s with the 75mm gun included 254 M4A3E2s. The M4A3E2 was an assault tank (nicknamed 'Jumbo') built for the close support of infantry in the Normandy campaign. Additional armour was welded to the frontal surfaces to increase the thickness to 4in and a new turret was designed with 6in of frontal armour; additional rolled plate was also added to the hull top. The weight of the tank was 42 tons compared with an ordinary M4A3's 31–34 tons. Some M4A3E2s were re-armed with a 76mm gun in the field. The 254 M4A3E2s were produced at the Grand Blanc Tank Arsenal in May and June 1944.

M4A4 Another extemporized engine was used in this model, this time developed by Chrysler. It featured five 6-cylinder engines on a common shaft. It was first used in the M3A4 built at Detroit Arsenal, and was continued in use in the M4A4. Due to the size of this engine it was necessary to lengthen the rear of the hull and re-space the bogies accordingly. This was the most distinctive distinguishing feature of this model. The Chrysler Multibank engine was considered complicated by the Ordnance Department and the M4A4 was the first model to be phased out of production in September 1943. The M4A4 was a major type supplied to the British.

Total production was 7499, all with 75mm guns. British designation for the M4A4 was Sherman V.

M4A5 There was no M4A5 as such; this designation was used by the US Ordnance Department as a 'paper' designation for the Ram, built and developed in Canada and based closely on the M4 design. The Ram, which did not see combat service, represented an interesting mix of British and American design features.

Left M4 (Sherman I) and British troops in the Italian campaign, 1944. *Below* Sherman Firefly with 17pdr gun spearheads the advance in Northern France, 1944. *Bottom* A very late production model, M4A3 with 76mm gun and horizontal volute suspension (HVSS), supports an advance by lorried British infantry in Korea, September 30, 1950.

M4A6 As a proposed replacement for the earlier interim engines the Ordnance Department selected the Caterpillar D-200A diesel motor after a series of competitive trials. Under the Ordnance designation RD-1820, this was used to replace the Chrysler engine in the M4A4, the resulting new model becoming the M4A6. However, at the end of 1943 it was decided to standardize on the Ford and Continental engined models only, and M4A6 production came to a premature end. Like the M4A4, the M4A6 had a lengthened rear hull to accommodate the engine, and wider spaced bogies.

Total production was 75, all with 75 mm guns. The British designation for the M4A6 was Sherman VII.

Sherman Firefly About 600 British Shermans were adapted to take the British high velocity 17pdr gun as the main armament. These were ready in time for the Normandy campaign and played a vital part against the Panthers and Tigers. Initially, until the supply of 17pdr guns improved, there was one of these up-gunned tanks per troop. When armed with the 17pdr the tank was called the Sherman Firefly. Nearly all marks of Sherman were used as Fireflies, but the most numerous was the Sherman V. When fitted with a 17pdr the suffix C was added, i.e. Sherman IC, IIC, IIIC, IVC, VC.

The initial design had twin fixed machine guns in the hull front as in the M3 series, and early vehicles appeared so fitted. The value of these weapons was limited, however, and they were soon removed to simplify production. Similarly vision ports initially provided for the driver and assistant driver were soon eliminated

One of the celebrated Sherman Fireflies (Sherman Mk VC) with its powerful 17pdr gun, stalks Tiger and Panther tanks with characteristic stealth along the hedgerows of the 'bocage' country.

Medium Tank M4A3 with others, in a defensive 'leaguer' while waiting to move forward for the crossing of the River Saar. Nearest is a late production vehicle with the modified, simplified hull front produced in 1944.

and were replaced by periscopes.

The main (75mm) gun and co-axial (·30 calibre) machine gun were in a mantlet designated Combination Gun Mount M34 on early production vehicles. This offered armoured protection for the 75mm gun only, and in later vehicles an improved mount, M34A1, was introduced (approved in October 1942) which had a full width armour shield. A final basic change was the use of a cast one-piece nose transmission cover in place of the three-piece bolted assembly initially used. Most later vehicles were also fitted with sand shields.

Design Improvements for the M4

The quest for more powerful gun armament was met by the introduction of the 76mm (3in) high velocity weapon, based on an earlier AA gun. The US Ordnance Department carried out design work in July–August 1942 and the weapon was tested in September 1942 fitted in a standard turret. This proved too small to hold the gun comfortably and in 1943 the large cylindrical turret of the T23 medium tank, which had a 90mm gun and which would fit in the turret ring of the M4 without alteration, was successfully adapted to hold the 76mm gun and was subsequently used in all models in the M4 series produced with this gun. The T23 (progenitor of the M26) was a medium tank design planned to succeed the M4 but was never standardized and was produced only in small numbers.

Production of the up-gunned M4 was authorized by Ordnance in February 1944, and the first M4A3s with new turret and armament were leaving the line at Detroit Arsenal in the following month. Detroit built 2845 M4A3 76mm vehicles that year and the type played an important part in the fighting in France and Germany with Patton's Third Army. Fisher commenced making the M4A3 76mm in September 1944 after completing 2845 M4A3 wet stowage tanks (see below) with the 75mm gun. Other Sherman variants fitted with the new gun and turret were the M4, M4A1, and M4A2. The 76mm M1A1 gun fired 3in ammunition with muzzle velocity, range, and penetrating power much superior to the 75mm M3 gun. The 3in APC shell M62 had a muzzle velocity of 2600fps, a maximum range of 16100yd and would penetrate 4in of face-hardened armour at a range of 1000yd. An azimuth indicator and elevation quadrant was provided for indirect fire control up to maximum range, and provision was made for direct fire control up to 3000yd. A full-width cast mantlet held the gun and there was a co-axial ·30 calibre machine gun. Small improvements resulted in the M1A1C and M1A2 guns which

were virtually identical to the original M1A1 gun except for the fitting of a muzzle brake.

A major change in models with welded hulls introduced with the T23 turret and 76mm gun was the 47 degree hull front. This steeper front eliminated the raised driver's hatchways and so greatly simplified production, and also offered a marginal improvement in protection. At the same time the steeper hull front also allowed larger access hatches for the driver and assistant driver. A gun barrel travelling clamp was incorporated on the new front plate.

Coincidentally with the revised hull came the so-called 'wet stowage' for the ammunition which was sited inside the vertical superstructure faces. Originally conventional 'dry' racks had been used, but the frequency of fires led to new racks being designed which had an outer

Below M4A3 (76mm) followed by M4A3 as US 7th Army units move through Bavaria in May 1945. Note the 47-degree hull front and large turret. *Bottom* Sandbags, track shoes, and other defensive pieces were often used to compensate for the M4's relatively thin armour.

A tank destroyer based on the M4 medium tank was the M10 3 in gun motor carriage. It had a sloped hull, well armoured, and an open-topped turret. This vehicle has 'prongs', extemporized cutters for carving through hedge-rows. Some of these vehicles were supplied to the British.

'hollow' casing containing a mixture of water and glycerine to reduce hazards from combustion. Wet stowage involved an extensive re-arrangement of the vehicle's interior, with no less than 2500 design changes.

One further armament variation was the fitting of the 105 mm howitzer to the M4 and M4A3 to provide a close-support tank to equip the HQ Companies of medium tank battalions in place of the small M8 self-propelled 75 mm gun. The mount was standardized as the M52. Detroit Arsenal built all 105 mm Shermans and the first models left the line in February 1944, production ceasing in March 1945 with 1641 vehicles built. Production of M4A3 105 mm – differing only in engine installation – commenced in May 1944 and ceased in June 1945 with a total of 3039 vehicles built. The new cupola and the new hull front were incorporated in these vehicles but turret traverse was by hand only. A further detail was the provision of a towing hook for an ammunition trailer.

Finally, in the list of design improvements, there was the introduction of horizontal volute spring suspension (HVSS) in place of the verti-cal volute type. HVSS was designed to give improved flotation and simpler maintenance. Track width with HVSS was increased from the original 16½ in to 23 in and each bogie had four wheels with the return rollers attached directly to the chassis sides. Any wheel could be removed and replaced without disturbing any adjacent wheels. With the old vertical volute suspension minor damage sometimes necessitated removing the complete bogie to carry out repairs. HVSS and its associated wide track T66, was developed late in 1943 and was fitted to the M4 series vehicles in production from late 1944 onwards. Shermans with this suspension were nicknamed 'Easy Eights' from the E8 designation applied to the vehicles which carried the trial installation.

Apart from the special track for HVSS vehicles, which was of rubber chevron type, the earlier vehicles could be fitted with any of four different types of track, all of which were inter-changeable. These were rubber bloc, steel, rub-ber chevron, or steel chevron. The steel tracks were introduced to conserve rubber and in practice they were found almost as good and durable as the rubber type. In certain theatres such as Italy, steel tracks were mainly used, but whatever the theories, the different types were usually well mixed at any given time. To increase the effective width of the tracks, extended end connectors (or 'grousers') were supplied which extended overall shoe width by a quarter for use in muddy or icy conditions. A special grouser compartment was furnished in the rear super-structure to carry these.

Reworked Vehicles

In addition to the modified production vehicles which were being turned out in 1944, the same year saw a massive 'rework' programme in-volving 5,880 early production vehicles which were completely remanufactured in the main tank arsenals and by other medium tank pro-ducers. All models except the M4A6 were involved in this scheme and most were vehicles which had already seen extensive service with armoured divisions in the USA or Canada. Apart from a complete overhaul, new tracks, new wiring, and so on, some had new engines, guns and mantlets. A common fitting was appliqué armour on the sides of the hull and on the front quarters of the turret. Some had extra armour plates on the driver's hatchways as well. These reworked vehicles were widely seen in US armoured divisions in Europe in 1944–45, where they were used as replacements or to supplement new vehicles. The M4s supplied to the French armoured divisions were also from the rework programme.

The British also reworked many of the vehicles supplied to them (also receiving re-worked vehicles direct from the USA). Most common addition seen on many vehicles was appliqué armour on the hull sides over the ammunition racks and this became a standard 'in service' modification as well. Two plates were added on the right side and one on the left, all spot-welded in positions corresponding to the ammunition rack positions. Spare track shoes, sand bags and even metal sheets were used in other 'in service' attempts to improve the armour protection of the M4, which was thin by the standards of 1944-45.

Anatomy of the Sherman

It will be apparent from the production story that though there were numerous different models of the Sherman, the basic vehicle was essentially the same whoever the manufacturer was. Only the engines and minor details differed between models.

All M4 series medium tanks (M4, M4A1, M4A2, M4A3, M4A4, M4A6) were of the same general design and size, and carried the same armament (with the variation between 75mm, 76mm, and 105mm detailed earlier). All had identical transmissions, volute spring suspensions (vertical or horizontal), and shoe tracks (steel or rubber). Other identical units were the turret and turret platform, gyro-stabilizer, combination turret gun mount and ·30 calibre bow gun mount.

The tank crew consisted of five men. The driver sat at the left bow of the tank, to the left of the transmission. The assistant driver's position was in the right bow, to the right of the transmission and directly behind the bow machine gun. The tank commander was stationed at the rear of the turret, just to the right of the main gun guard. The gunner's station was almost directly in front of the commander. The loader's station was to the left of the main gun.

For each of the five crew stations there was a periscope, all except the gunner's mounted so that they could be rotated for observation in any direction and tilted to raise or lower the line of vision. The gunner's periscope was connected to the gun mount by linkage that kept the line of vision in constant alignment with the gun as the gun was elevated or depressed. This periscope was fitted with a telescope sight so mounted that it could be moved independently of the periscope and the gun for gun laying.

For the driver and assistant driver, direct vision was provided by horizontal slots in the hull front plate. The slots were fitted with heavy protective covers. In late vehicles, however, these slots were deleted.

A periscope in a revolving mount in the turret hatch was provided for the use of the tank commander when the hatch was closed. All late production vehicles of the 1944-45 period, however, had a new vision cupola with six episcopes which offered a great improvement over the original arrangement.

Access to the tank was provided by two hatches in the bow and a revolving hatch in the turret. For use in an emergency, a quick-opening escape hatch was provided in the tank floor behind the assistant driver.

All models had a radio and an interphone system for crew communication. The radio and interphone were shock-mounted on a common base located on a shelf in the turret bulge.

The turret carried a combination mount for a 75mm gun and a ·30 calibre machine gun. The turret platform, or basket, rotated with the turret, which could be traversed through 360 degrees either by hand cranks or by electric-hydraulic drive. The combination gun mount allowed the gun to be elevated 25 degrees above the horizontal and depressed 10 degrees.

The turret guns could be manually elevated or depressed by operating the elevating hand-wheel. When the gyrostabilizer was in operation, the gun was elevated by hydraulic power controlled by the elevating hand wheel, and the gyrostabilizer automatically held the gun steady at any quadrant angle of elevation at which it

Top Flamethrower devices fitted to M4 medium tanks were widely used in the Pacific campaigns to burn out Japanese strongholds in the jungle. The leading tank in this photograph is burning out a bunker with a flamethrower at point-blank range while infantry wait to move forward. Hollandia, April 1944.

Above British Sherman Mk III (M4A2) in Tunisia, April 1943.

Sherman DD (Duplex Drive), a British development for amphibious operations, showing the canvas side screens folded and rear propellers stowed. The propellers drove from power take-off in the transmission. Struts and inflatable tubes held up the canvas screens. *Below* A famous improvization was the fitting of 60-pound aircraft rockets to turrets by some regiments of the Guards Armoured Division in 1944. This made a potent terror weapon, if not an accurate one. *Bottom* T34 Calliope was a 4·6 inch rocket launcher frame carried on an M4. These vehicles were used in relatively small numbers in 1944–45.

had been laid, while the tank was in motion. The two turret guns were fired electrically by means of the firing buttons (foot-operated switches) to the left of the gunner.

The vehicle was steered by means of levers, which operated steering brakes in the differential housing. Braking was effected by pulling back both steering brakes at once.

M4 Special Purpose and Miscellaneous Types

Special purpose types which saw full production and service in the US Army were relatively few. On the other hand the number of experimental prototypes developed by the US Ordnance Department ran into dozens, many of them of a very sophisticated nature. This reflected the rift between the designers, the Ordnance Department, and the users, Army Ground Forces, who were resistant to the introduction of special service vehicles except where the need was quite obvious. (This same attitude led to the delay in the service introduction of up-gunned models of the Sherman, and indeed of the Sherman's successor, the M26 Pershing).

It was due to this that the special purpose types used by the US Army in North-West Europe in 1944–45 were mainly of British origin: the Sherman Crab (US designation, Mine Exploder T2) and the Sherman DD 'swimming' tank, which was subsequently adopted for production in the USA in 1945 as the Sherman DD III, the DD I and DD II being the original British conversions some of which were used by US battalions in the Normandy landings.

M32 Tank Recovery Vehicle The major special type developed by the Americans was the Tank Recovery Vehicle M32 which saw widespread service from late 1943. This was a modification based on the standard M4 hull. The turret was removed and replaced by a fixed superstructure and a 60000lb winch in the space formerly taken by the turret cage. An 18ft A-frame jib was pivoted at the forward end of the hull and normally lay to the rear. For operations such as engine changing it could be topped up and rigged forward. The vehicle was unarmed, but an 81mm mortar was fixed to the front end of the superstructure firing forward; this was used solely for smoke bombs to give cover during recovery operations. In practice, however, the mortar was frequently removed, evidently because it obstructed winching operations.

Various models of the M4 were converted to M32s, the differences being restricted only to the basic model changes already described. Specifically these were M32 (M4 chassis), M32B1 (M4A1 chassis – cast hull), M32B2 (M4A2 chassis), M32B3 (M4A3 chassis), M32B4 (M4A4 chassis). The M32 weighed 62000lb. Some were delivered to the British (designated Sherman ARV Mk III) and to other M4 series users.

Rocket Launchers A large number of rocket launcher types were developed, most important of which was the T34 Calliope. This simple but effective conversion consisted essentially of a bank of rockets in a carrier frame mounted above the turret. In the T34 there were 60 4·6in rocket tubes in four rows. Elevation of the frame was controlled by a linking arm from the gun barrel, and traverse was effected by training the turret on the required bearing. When the rockets were expended the mount could be jettisoned if necessary.

The Calliope was a 'limited procurement' type first used by the US 2nd Armored Division in August 1944. It was a formidable weapon for putting down a huge blanket barrage in softening-up bombardments. Variations on this theme were the T34E1 and T34E2 which had different arrangements of the launchers.

Of other rocket launcher types, the only ones to see limited service were the T40 (M17) Whiz-bang and the T99. The Whiz-bang was similar to the Calliope in arrangement but had 20 7·2in rockets and a box-like frame enclosing the tubes. The T99 had two small box-like launcher frames, one each side of the turret, each with 22 4·5in rockets. Some M4A3s with T99 launchers were used in the Pacific in 1945.

Flamethrowers Flamethrowers in US service mostly took the form of the E4R2, R3 or R4 types (M3-4-3) or the E6 type. These were supplied in kit form for installation in the field. The former fitted in place on the hull MG, and the latter fitted above the assistant driver's hatch in a periscope type mount. Another flamethrower type was the POA, mainly used by the US Marine Corps, in which the flame projector replaced the main gun. In Europe the US 2nd Armored Division used a British-developed flamethrower, the Crocodile, four of which were fitted to Shermans.

Mine exploders Mine exploders were developed by the score for fitting to the M4, and these covered all forms of mine clearing: excavating, flailing, and pressure. Only a few saw service, the rest progressing no further than the trials stage. Of these the Mine Exploder T1E1, Earthworm, was designed for the M32. It took the form of three disc units arranged tricycle fashion and suspended from the jib of the M32 with a heavy girder frame supporting the discs.

A better device was the Mine Exploder T1E3, Aunt Jemima, which reached 'limited standard' status as the Mine Exploder M1; 75 vehicles were built and were used in Italy and France in 1944. Two huge 10ft diameter disc-type rollers were pushed ahead of the vehicle, drive coming via a chain from the vehicle's sprockets. While effective in exploding mines, the Aunt Jemima was very cumbersome and in muddy conditions it usually needed a second tank to push the carrier vehicle.

Subsequently British Sherman Crabs (Mine

Sherman Crab flail tank was developed for mine-sweeping and was an important type in 1944–45. The chain flail rotor was driven from front sprockets and lifted hydraulically.

Exploder T2) were taken over by US troops and became the main type in use. In addition some units, notably in the US Marine Corps, improvized mine exploders of their own based on the flail idea and often using the arms of the standard M1 dozer blade which was supplied for field fitting to the M4.

Self-propelled Guns

While all variants of the M4 series were used as a basis for the special purpose and miscellaneous types, the M4A3 chassis was mainly used for the various self-propelled guns that formed part of the equipment of the US armoured divisions. This reflected the US policy of keeping the Ford-engined vehicles for first-line operations. The Gun and Howitzer Motor Carriages on M4 series chassis were:

M7B1 HMC The M7 (known to the British as the Priest) with its 105mm howitzer was originated on the M3 Medium chassis, but when the M4 superseded the M3 in production, M7s were built on the M4A3 chassis and designated M7B1.

M10 GMC The M10 3in gun tank destroyer was built on an adapted diesel-engined M4A2 chassis with a new flat-topped hull and open-topped turret. Production was continued on the M4A3 chassis and this Ford-engined version was designated M10A1. M10 production totalled 6596 of which 2603 were M10A1 built between June 1942 and December 1943.

M36 GMC Developed from November 1943 to provide a heavier gun (the 90mm AA gun) on the M10 chassis. By May 1945 M36 production totalled 2324 of which 187 were M36B1 produced on standard M4A3 hull and 1268 were converted M10s and M10A1s.

The M36 could take on all German tanks. One unit, the 702nd Tank Destroyer Bn. of the US 2nd Armored Division, chalked up the fantastic score between 16th and 30th November 1944 of one PzKpfw IV, fifteen Panthers, one King Tiger, two self-propelled guns, two anti-tank guns, two pillboxes, and two half-tracks, all totally destroyed for the loss of only eight of its own vehicles.

M40 155mm gun motor carriage was based on the hull and drive of the Ford-engined M4A3. Introduced in 1944 this successful weapon was still in service over 20 years later.

M4s press on, leading the Allied advance across Europe in 1944–45, when the M4 was the Allies' most numerous and successful tank. These are 7th Army vehicles in Alsace, January 1945.

M40 GMC One of the most successful heavy self-propelled weapons ever to see service, the M40 design started life in December 1943 as a successor to the M12 (1918 pattern 155mm gun on M3 chassis). It mounted the M2 155mm gun 'Long Tom' on a widened M4A3 chassis with HVSS. The engine was moved forward and a recoil spade and working platform added at the rear. Total production between January 1945 (when production began at Pressed Steel) and the end of the war in Europe was 311. The M40 fought in North West Europe (its first action being in the bombardment of Cologne) and later in Korea.

M43 HMC Similar to the M40 but with an 8in howitzer. 48 were built.

The Sherman in Action

By 1944 the Sherman had reached the peak of its development and in its final form with HVSS and the 76mm gun, it proved equal to the 'blitzkrieg' role for which it was mainly used. Ironically the US armoured divisions in North West Europe at this time were using these tactics against the German Army which had demonstrated their effectiveness four years earlier. This time the German Army was on the defensive and had developed armour – such as the Tigers, Panthers, and the various heavy assault guns – more suitable for a defensive war than the lighter Panzers which spearheaded the armoured battles of 1939–42. No Sherman could – on paper – stand up to a Tiger or Panther, but the US Armies in North West Europe had the priceless advantage of supporting air power, adequate reserves, superb logistics, and overwhelming superiority of numbers. In these conditions, the tank became a component of a coordinated attack scheme. The main requirements were for mobility, reliability, and adequate armament, and the M4A3 Sherman 76mm had all of these qualities. In vast outflanking movements which avoided the heaviest enemy armour – leaving it to be dealt with by tank destroyers and aircraft – the Sherman was used as an instrument of advance and exploitation.

Exceptional distances like the 151 miles covered in 36 hours by a battalion of the 4th Armored Division during the Battle of the Bulge serve as an indication of the M4's true value as a fighting weapon.

Certainly the Sherman, best known and most widely produced tank in the history of armoured warfare, earns its place in posterity alone by its success against the German panzers in 1944–45. That it was also used by the armies of a dozen other nations and could still figure prominently in the Israeli–Egyptian wars of 1967 and 1973, when most of its contemporary designs remain only as museum exhibits, is remarkable, particularly if it is remembered that the Sherman was a utility design owing its development to the early successes of the German armoured forces it later was to trounce. Matched tank for tank, the Sherman was vastly inferior to its German opponents. But the Allies had the advantages of sheer weight of numbers, better maintenance, better logistics and, in the final analysis, better tactics. It might also be argued that the US Ordnance Board had better judgment than their German – or British – contemporaries by standardizing, centralizing production control and progressing with a standard design in the light of experience rather than waste time and capacity in a continual quest for alternative improved designs.

The British Infantry Tanks

The British infantry tanks, in essence, continued the original 1916 ideas of tank employment into the Second World War, although it soon turned out that the conditions were so different that the notion of a special type of tank to support infantry advances on foot were as outmoded as trench warfare. For the Second World War involved the very mobile employment of armour, and highly protected slow moving vehicles like infantry tanks had only limited value in many situations.

The story of the British infantry tanks, which culminated in the Matilda and Churchill tanks of the Second World War, started in April 1934 when the Research Committee of the Chief of the General Staff considered a paper presented by the Inspector-General of the Royal Tank Corps which dealt with requirements for a tank to co-operate with infantry – the category which later became known as the 'infantry tank'. This postulated two alternatives: (1) a very small and inconspicuous vehicle, heavily armoured, armed with machine guns, and available in numbers; (2) a bigger vehicle with a larger calibre gun and heavier armour able to engage enemy weapons as well as carrying machine guns for defence against enemy infantry. In both cases the vehicle was only required to move at walking pace, ie, infantry speed.

The General Staff drew up a specification based loosely on the second alternative, though they asked for either a ·5 in machine gun or a 2 pdr as main armament, with a minimum armour thickness of 1 in. Vickers designed the A9 tank, which later evolved into the Valentine tank, to this specification. Major General Sir Hugh Elles was appointed Master General of the Ordnance in May 1934, responsible for tank procurement. Elles had commanded the Tank

Corps in France in the First World War and as a result was a keen advocate of tanks for infantry support. He was persuaded that Vickers could design and build a prototype infantry tank to the 'small' specification but with increased armour, proof against any known calibre of anti-tank gun. Sir John Carden of Vickers (who had initiated the tankettes – Chapter 3) designed this vehicle, designated A11, and the pilot model A11E1 was delivered to the army for trials in September 1936.

To keep costs to a minimum, the A11 was very simple. A commercial Ford V-8 engine and transmission were used, with steering, brake and clutches adapted from the type used in the Vickers light tanks. The simple suspension was derived from that used on the Vickers Dragon gun tractors. Trials revealed the need for suspension improvements to prevent track shedding (the return rollers as a result being repositioned on the hull sides) and the need for a certain amount of splash proofing. A first production order for 60 vehicles was placed in April 1937 and this was later increased, a total of 140 vehicles (including the pilot model) being completed by August 1940 when production ceased.

Meanwhile, the limitations of machine gun armament were appreciated and design of the A12, Infantry Tank Mk II, was initiated in November 1936, the A11 being regarded as an interim type. The Infantry Tank Mk I equipped the 1st Army Tank Brigade in France in 1940 and proved almost immune to German anti-tank guns. However, its lack of hitting power meant that it had only limited tactical value and production was abandoned after the Dunkirk evacuation.

At the time the Infantry Tank Mk I pilot model was delivered, the Mechanization Board

The theory of the British infantry tank idea is well shown here, as infantry sections advance across open country behind the slow moving 'I' tanks during an exercise in France in January 1940. The small size of the Infantry Tank Mk I is apparent from the group in the background.

Cruiser Tank Mk I (the A9) was the forerunner of the Valentine and introduced the distinctive 'slow motion' suspension.

was already considering a 'scaled up' version with an extra crew member, a 2pdr gun or twin machine guns, and a speed of up to 15mph. A weight limit of 14 tons was imposed to meet current military bridging restrictions.

It soon became obvious that these requirements could not be incorporated in the basic A11 design since the turret alone, to hold a 2pdr gun, would bring the A11 weight up to 13 tons, and a new engine would also be required. Thus a completely new design was called for and was drawn up by the Mechanization Board on the basis of 60mm armour thickness, a commercial type AEC diesel engine, and heavy side skirts to protect the 'Japanese Type' suspension derived from that on the Vickers Medium Tank. The layout of the 'Matilda Senior' as it was called (properly designated A12 Infantry Tank Mk II), was based closely on that of the A7 medium tank which had been designed and built in prototype form only by Royal Ordnance Factory, Woolwich, in 1929–32.

In November 1936 Vulcan Foundry of Warrington were given contracts to produce wooden mock-ups and two mild steel pilot models of the A12 design. The mock-up was inspected in April 1937, by which time it had been decided to use twin AEC diesel engines coupled together and a Wilson epicyclic gearbox. Provision was to be made for mounting a 3in howitzer in close support models and various other detail points were settled at this early stage. Construction of the pilot model was, however, held up by delays in the delivery of the gearbox and other components and the A12E1 pilot was not ready until April 1938. Meanwhile an order 'off the drawing board' for 65 vehicles was given in December 1937, and this was soon increased to 165. Trials were generally satisfactory, but some small modifications were made to the gearbox and suspension. Cooling

was also improved and provision made for 'colonial' use by fitting air cleaners.

By this time re-armament was under way and the need for tanks was urgent. In June 1938 contracts for further vehicles were placed with Fowler and Ruston & Hornsby under Vulcan's 'parentage', and subsequently LMS, Harland & Wolff, and North British Locomotive all received contracts. For the later marks Leyland were brought in (in 1940) to make engines. Total output of A12s was 2987 and production ceased in August 1943.

The A12 did not lend itself to easy mass-production however, due to the size and shape of the armour castings used in the design. There was particular difficulty in making the one-piece armour side skirts and the number of mud chutes was reduced from six (in the pilot model) to five (in production models) to facilitate producing this component. By the outbreak of war with Germany in September 1939 there were only two A12s in service; by early 1940 a number had been issued to 7th Royal Tank Regiment in France, where they were used with success in the Battle of Arras just prior to the Dunkirk evacuation.

With withdrawal of the A11, Matilda I, the terms 'Matilda Senior' and 'Matilda II' were dropped, and the A12 was known simply as the Matilda. The Matilda is best remembered for its important part in the early Western Desert campaigns. In Libya in 1940 it was virtually immune to any Italian anti-tank gun or tank and Matildas reigned supreme until the appearance of the German 88mm Flak gun in the anti-tank role in mid-1941; this was the first gun able to penetrate Matilda's heavy armour at long range. It was not possible to fit the 6pdr gun in the Matilda (though an attempt was made to mount the A27 type turret on a Matilda chassis), due to the small size of the turret and turret ring. Thus in 1942, the Matilda declined in importance as a gun tank and was last used in action in this role at the first Alamein battle in July 1942.

From then on, the Matilda was used in secondary roles for special purposes. Most important was its development as a mine-clearing vehicle, the extensive minefields laid by the Afrika Korps being cleared by Matilda Scorpions. These were power-driven chain beaters which detonated the mines forward of the tank. A further development was the Matilda Baron, also a mine clearer. This was the start of a major employment of infantry tanks in specialized battlefield roles by the British, who became the innovators in this field.

The Valentine

The Infantry Tank Mk III was altogether different, the famous Valentine tank. In 1938, Vickers

Infantry Tank Mk II, Matilda, was Britain's best armoured tank in 1940 and remained so until heavier anti-tank guns came into use. This is a Matilda of the Tobruk garrison in 1942.

A reluctant Matilda is towed home by an artillery tractor after a desert engagement.

Infantry Tank Mk III, the Valentine, seen on exercises in 1941.

Sherman IIC Firefly, with
17pdr gun, of the Pakistan
Army, during the Indo-
Pakistan war of 1967.

were among the first approached to join the Infantry Tank Mk II (A12) production group under Vulcan. As an alternative they were invited to build a design of their own based on the A9 and A10 which had been the first 'infantry tanks' to emanate from the 1934 General Staff specification for this type. The A10 had subsequently been reclassified as a 'heavy cruiser' since it was much less heavily armoured than the A11 and A12 designs. Vickers chose to submit their own design since they already had production facilities and experience which would have been wasted if they had switched to building A12s. The new vehicle utilized a chassis, suspension, engine and transmission identical to the A10 but had a lower, more heavily armoured superstructure and an entirely new turret mounting a 2pdr gun. Plans were very quickly drawn up and submitted to the War Office just prior to St. Valentine's Day in February 1938, and this date suggested the name 'Valentine' by which the vehicle was subsequently known.

More than a year passed before a production order was placed, however. The main design shortcoming in the view of the General Staff was the small turret, which would only accommodate two men. In July 1939, with war looming and an urgent need for tanks in quantity, an order for 275 vehicles was placed with Vickers straight off the drawing board. Quick production had been promised by Vickers since the chassis had already been proven with the A10, so that no lengthy development period was required. The first production vehicle was delivered to the Army for trials in May 1940 and proved very satisfactory; it provided a stable gun platform and was mechanically reliable. First service deliveries were made in late 1940 and for a period in 1940–41 Valentines were used in the cruiser tank role in armoured divisions to help overcome the shortage of cruiser tanks. The first Valentines appeared with tank brigades in the 8th Army in June 1941 and subsequently played an important part in the remainder of the desert fighting.

Valentine production ceased in early June 1944 after a total of 8275 vehicles had been completed. By late 1942, however, the Valentine was largely obsolete due to its low speed and small turret which restricted the fitting of larger calibre armament. Mks III and V had the turret modified to accommodate three men (a loader in addition to commander and gunner), but the third turret member was, of necessity, dropped when the 6pdr gun was fitted in later marks. In this case the inadequacy of a two man turret crew was accepted in the interests of increased gun power. The 6pdr gun was introduced into production Valentines from March 1942. Other modifications included an improved engine

installation (a GMC diesel unit) and a change over from all riveted to all welded construction. In March 1943 a Valentine was used for the test installation and firing of the British 75 mm tank gun, intended for the A27 cruiser tanks and the Churchill, and the success of these trials in the Valentine led to the development of a production version mounting this gun. This version (Mk XI) was the final production variant. Valentines were built by Metropolitan-Cammell and Birmingham Carriage & Wagon in addition to Vickers. They were also built in Canada by the Canadian Pacific Railway Co. in Montreal. Of the 1420 Canadian vehicles produced, however, all but 30 – which were retained for training – were delivered to the Soviet Army. The Valentine was the only Allied tank supplied under Lend-Lease for which the Russians asked for more, and the only type acknowledged in Soviet official war histories.

The Valentine was one of the most important British tanks and in 1943 totalled nearly one quarter of British tank output. Valentines formed the basis of many special purpose AFVs including bridgelayers, mineclearers, and amphibious (DD) tanks. These are summarized below. Two SP guns were also put into production on the Valentine chassis, the Bishop 25 pdr, and the Archer 17 pdr tank destroyer, the latter remaining in service until about 1960.

Valentine OP/Command Converted gun tank with dummy gun and extra communications equipment for battery commanders and OP officers of Archer-equipped SP units, 1944.

Valentine Scorpion II Valentine tank with turret removed and replaced with armoured cabin for flail operator and rotor drive engine. This conversion was produced in Britain in mid-1943 and the Scorpion equipment was derived from that developed in the Middle East for fitting to the Matilda. It was not used operationally since it was replaced from late 1943 by the Sherman Crab; Scorpion was used for training however. This vehicle could also tow Centipede anti-mine rollers. A large counterweight was fitted at the hull rear on the Valentine Scorpion to balance the weight of the rotor arms in front.

Valentine AMRA Mk Ib This was a Valentine gun tank adapted to propel anti-mine roller attachment (AMRA).

Valentine Snake Valentine rigged to tow Snake equipment – an explosive-filled pipe towed across a suspected mine-field then detonated to blow a passage through the mines. A few were so used in 8th Army.

Valentine Bridgelayer This was a Valentine II with turret removed and adapted to carry a 30ft scissors bridge. Hydraulic rams and arms were fitted for launch and recovery and hy-

Valentines were supplied under Lend-Lease to Russia in 1942. These Soviet Valentines are in the Caucasus.

Archer was an SP gun development of the Valentine. The 17pdr gun fires to the rear.

draulic equipment was fitted in turret space. It was mainly used for training, 1943–44, and the Churchill Bridgelayer replaced it for operational use.

Valentine DD (Mks III and VIII) The DD (Duplex Drive) idea was evolved by Nicholas Straussler, a Hungarian-born military engineer, and the system involved a propeller driven by power take-off from the vehicle's engine. To provide flotation, collapsible canvas side screens were fitted to the vehicle's hull which, when raised, gave a boat-like form to the vehicle. The actual tank hull was, in fact, suspended below the water surface. The Valentine was selected as the standard DD tank, the design was finalized in June 1942, and 650 Mks III and VIII were converted accordingly. They were mainly used for crew training and for developing operational techniques. In late 1943 the Sherman was similarly adapted and the DD brigades of 79th Armoured Division which took part in Opera-

tion Overlord and subsequent operations in North West Europe were equipped with the latter type.

Valentine Flamethrowers To determine the best system for a tank-mounted flame projector, the Petroleum Warfare Department (formed in June 1940) modified two Valentine tanks in 1941, one with a projector ignited by cordite charges and one with a projector operated by gas (nitrogen) pressure. The fuel was carried in a trailer and the flame projector was mounted on the hull front. Trials started in 1942 showed the gas-operated system to be the best, and from this test installation was developed the Crocodile equipment for the Churchill flamethrower used in the North West Europe campaign in 1944–45. The trailer of the Crocodile was essentially the same as that used with the Valentine, with the addition of an armoured superstructure. Neither Valentine flamethrower variant was used operationally.

The Super Sherman is an effective modification of the Second World War vintage M4 Sherman tank which has served the Israeli Defence Forces well for many years. Essentially, this is the basic Sherman tank re-engined and with a 105 mm gun of French origin in an extended turret. These examples are shown in service during the 'Yom Kippur' War of 1973.

The Churchill Tank

At the outbreak of war in September 1939, there was a strong school of opinion at the British War Office (soon to be proved wrong) that conditions on the Western Front would not be very different from conditions experienced in 1914–18. There was therefore a need for a very heavy infantry tank invulnerable to known anti-tank guns, with a very wide trench-crossing ability, and able to negotiate ground churned up by shell fire. Designated A20, a specification was drawn up by the Superintendent of Tank Design, Woolwich, and Harland & Wolff were asked to build a pilot model. Armour thickness of 80mm, speed of 15mph, ability to climb a 5ft parapet, and a crew of seven were among characteristics requested. Essentially the A20 was a refinement of the rhomboid shape tanks built by the British in 1916–18 (Chapter 1); various combinations of armament were considered including a 6pdr, French 75mm, 2in howitzer, and a 2pdr. Finally a 2pdr was selected for the turret, another to be mounted in the nose, with machine guns recessed in the hull side at the front. Four pilot models were ordered in February 1940. The first pilot model ran trials in June 1940, plagued by gearbox trouble. Data from the first run, however, showed that

in order to maintain the required performance the gun armament would have to be reduced to a single 2pdr.

This coincided with the Dunkirk evacuation, when Britain was left with less than 100 tanks for home defence. Vauxhall (the British subsidiary of General Motors) were therefore asked to 'refine' the A20 design, scale it down slightly, and get it into production as rapidly as possible, preferably within a year. Choice of Vauxhall was largely influenced by the fact that their Vauxhall-Bedford twin-six truck engine was scheduled for the A20. The A20 pilot model and plans were handed over to Vauxhall, extra draughtsmen were loaned by the Mechanization Board, and a pilot model of the new design, A22, Infantry Tank Mk IV, was ready by November 1940. The first 14 production models were delivered in June 1941 from an order for 500 straight off the drawing board. Due to the rushed development programme for this vehicle, there were numerous defects in the design leading to frequent breakdowns with the early marks. This necessitated considerable re-work programmes in 1942–43, the secondment of Vauxhall engineers to units equipped with the tank, and numerous detail improvements to mechanical components.

Named Churchill, the A22 was built in quantity by a production group consisting of Broom & Wade, Birmingham Carriage & Wagon, Metropolitan Cammell, Charles Roberts, Newton Chambers, Gloucester Railway Carriage, Leyland, Dennis and Harland & Wolff, all under the 'parentage' of Vauxhall.

The Churchill was of composite construction consisting of an inner skin of $\frac{1}{2}$in mild steel with an outer covering of armour plate bolted or riveted in position. Initially a cast turret was fitted, but later models had larger turrets of either cast, welded, or composite construction. The engine and drive were at the rear, and the overall tracks with small sprung bogie assemblies allowed space between the lower and upper runs of track for stowage of ammunition and stores, making the Churchill an unusually roomy vehicle. Escape doors for the crew were fitted in each side. Transmission featured the new Merritt-Brown four-speed gearbox which provided controlled differential steering, the Churchill being the first British tank to have this.

Armament of the Mk I was a 2pdr with a 3in howitzer in the hull front. Changing tactical requirements, however, led to a change of armament through the Churchill's production life. In common with the British cruiser tanks a 6pdr gun was fitted in 1942, necessitating a larger turret (Mk III). Experience in the desert fighting of 1941–42 led the War office to believe that speed and reliability were more important than heavy armour, and it was decided to cease Churchill production in 1943 when the A27 series of cruiser tanks became available. However, the Churchill's first combat actions, with the 1st Army in the Tunisian campaign, proved most successful in the hilly conditions of the terrain and this earned the vehicle a reprieve. In 1943, the Churchill was again up-gunned (Mk VII) with the new British version of the 75 mm gun. At the same time major design improvements were effected.

Since it was built to meet British railway loading gauge restrictions, the Churchill suffered from the same disadvantage as other

contemporary British designs – it was too narrow to take the larger turret required for the 17pdr gun. Thus by 1944–45 it was undergunned by German standards, although this was offset to an extent by the vehicle's heavy armour protection.

The other factor which made the Churchill one of the most important British tanks of 1939–45 was its adaptability to the specialized armour roles needed for the invasion of Europe in 1944. The vehicle's roomy interior, regular shape, and heavy armour made it particularly useful as an armoured engineer vehicle, bridgelayer or recovery vehicle. The many variants built for these specialized roles are summarized below. Finally there were many experimental variants of the Churchill and the most important of these are also outlined.

The specialized versions of the Churchill were developed by a special unit, 79th Armoured Division, actually a huge organization by 1944. The armour specials – known as 'funnies' – made a major contribution to the development of armoured warfare and all the successful special types have been since perpetuated by all the great armies since 1945. Some items were distinctly 'Heath Robinson' in design, but the key equipment, bridgelayers, flails, and assault vehicles proved their worth and have been refined continuously over the years since 1945.

Churchill Crocodile Flamethrowing was tested and proved in the Valentine tank and it was decided to standardize on a gas pressure system. In October 1943 the Churchill VII was chosen, and was given a link system for a trailer and a protected belly tank to a flame gun projector in the forward hull. Churchill VIIs were built for adaptation to the Crocodile role as required. The vehicle's main armament could

Top The A20 prototype from which the eventual Churchill tank design was evolved.

Above Infantry Tank Mk IV, Churchill Mk I. This very first mark had a 3 in howitzer in the nose.

Left Infantry Tank Mk II, Matilda IV, was, in 1940–41, Britain's most heavily armoured tank and was one of the most successful until the Germans developed anti-tank guns powerful enough to knock it out. Matilda was most widely used in the earlier stages of the campaign in the Western Desert. *Far left* Infantry Tank Mk III, Valentine I, a Vickers design rushed into production in 1940 to supplement the Matilda.

Above Valentines of 6th Armoured Division lined up for a royal inspection in 1942. These Valentines were used in the cruiser tank role even though officially they were infantry tanks.

Top Churchill VI; note the cast turret.

Above Churchill Crocodile flamethrowers passing US infantry on their way to the attack.

taking fortified open beaches. Urgently shown to be necessary was a heavily armoured vehicle to carry and support assault engineers charged with breaching heavy defences. Lt. Donovan of the Royal Canadian Engineers proposed adapting an existing tank. Both the Ram and Sherman were evaluated for the role, but the choice fell on the Churchill, which had a roomier hull plus side escape doors which were useful for egress under fire. A spigot mortar, called a Petard, of 29cm calibre and firing a 40lb bomb 80 yards, was developed, tested in a Covenanter tank, and modified for fitting on the 6pdr mount of the Churchill III or IV. 180 Churchills of these marks were converted to AVREs by D-Day, June 6, 1944, and equipped the 1st Assault Brigade of 79th Armoured Division at this time. Subsequently another 574 vehicles were converted and AVREs played an important part in the North West Europe campaign. AVREs were fitted to carry and drop fascines (brushwood bundles), the CIRD (Canadian Indestructible Roller Device) for mine-clearing, and SBG (Small Box Girder) bridges, attachment points being incorporated for all these to be handled as required. A few AVREs were unarmed or lacked the usual AVRE fittings, these being used mainly for training. Also produced for use with the AVRE was a sledge for towing stores, fascines, or explosives. Further AVRE development took place after the war, again with the Churchill as a basis, and the Churchill VII AVRE remained in British service until the mid-1960s, long after Churchills had disappeared as gun tanks.

Churchill ARV Mk I The Armoured Recovery Vehicle (ARV) was a Churchill I or II with turret removed, stores carried in turret space, and fitted to carry demountable A-frame jib front or rear.

Churchill ARV Mk II Churchill III or IV chassis with turret removed and replaced by fixed box-like dummy turret and dummy gun. It was fitted with demountable jibs, front and rear, earth spade at rear, and two-speed winch with 25 (long) tons pull. It was produced in 1944 and used for many years after the war.

Churchill Ark Mk I A further lesson learnt from the Dieppe raid was the need for armoured bridge-carrying vehicles able to lay ramps across sea walls or span defence ditches and craters so that following vehicles could cross. Late in 1943, the 79th Armoured Division built an experimental version of the Churchill with the turret removed, timber trackways above the hull top, and ramps supported by kingposts and hinged at each end of the trackways. This was successfully tested and 50 further conversions of this type were ordered in February 1944, using Churchill II and IV chassis which

still be used, of course. Range of the Crocodile was 80–120 yards in 80 one-second bursts from a full trailer. When empty or hit the trailer could be jettisoned. Trailer weighed 6½ (long) tons. Used in North West Europe in 1944–45, the total production was 800 Crocodile units by May 1945, with 250 earmarked for the Far East.

Churchill AVRE (AVRE: Armoured Vehicle, Royal Engineers.) Though the Anglo-Canadian Dieppe raid in 1943 was unsuccessful it proved that specialized types of armour were needed to assist assault forces in landing on and

had originally been earmarked for CDL use. ('Ark': Armoured Ramp Carrier.)

Churchill Ark Mk II (UK Pattern) In July 1944 modifications were made to an existing Ark which involved doubling the width of the left hand trackway from 2ft to 4ft, allowing 'B' vehicles with narrow track centres to use the Ark crossing facilities as well as tanks. This was successful and all Ark Is were converted to this form and designated Ark II. The suffix 'UK Pattern' was added to distinguish this type from a similar design evolved by 8th Army in Italy. Arks had their turret apertures plated in and a square cupola added. A kingpost at each end held the ramps upright while the vehicle was driven into the required position, either in a ditch, a river, or against a wall or bank. The ramps were dropped by a quick-release mechanism so forming a bridge for vehicles to cross. The Ark was considered expendable if need be and no provision was made for rehoisting the ramps, except by the aid of a recovery vehicle. Sections of the trackways could be removed for engine access. Arks had a crew of four. Standard ramp length was 12½ft, but longer ramps were tested and, on occasion, used for bridging extra wide gaps. There was also a 9ft long extension ramp which could be hinged to the end of the standard ramps if needed for specific tasks. There were some occasions when a deep gap was spanned by one Ark being driven onto another.

Churchill Ark Mk II (Italian Pattern) This was similar to the UK Pattern (as above), but utilized American made ramps which came in two different lengths, 12ft 3½in (M2) or 15ft 3in (M1) for fitting as required. Fundamental difference from the UK Pattern vehicle was the lack of built-up trackways on the hull top, the vehicle tracks themselves serving as trackways. The mode of operation was the same for both of these vehicles.

Churchill Bridgelayer Development of this vehicle started in 1942 and was based on experience gained with the Covenanter and Valentine Bridgelayers. Essentially this was a turretless Churchill III or IV (or VII from 1945–46) with hydraulic equipment fitted in the fighting compartment to work a pivoted arm which could launch the 30ft bridge horizontally from its stowage on the hull top and into position spanning a ditch or crater. The bridge was made in four parts for ease of handling but was carried, and launched, rigid. It could support vehicles up to 60 tons. Production vehicles were issued in 1944 and allocated at first in troops of three Brigade HQ of Churchill-equipped tank brigades. Later, as more vehicles became available, they were issued more widely. Crew of this vehicle was two. The bridge weighed 4·8 (long)

tons. From 1946 on, a heavier bridge was used on this vehicle and the vehicle remained in service until the early 1960s when the Centurion bridgelayer replaced it.

Churchill AVREs were also used operationally to propel various types of assault bridge used in combat. These included the Skid Bailey, a short bridge built from Bailey parts, mounted on skids, and pushed and pulled into place by two AVREs, and the Mobile Bailey Bridge which was a complete (Class 40) bridge mounted on dumb Orolo track units. Two AVREs were also used to propel this.

Top Churchill AVRE, with demolition gun.

Above Churchill VI demonstrates its ability, climbing over a Churchill ARK to scale a sea wall.

Far left Cruiser Tank Mk
IIA CS, a close support
tank of 1939 with 3·7 in
(95 mm) howitzer, was a
Vickers design from
which the Valentine
infantry tank was
developed.
Above Infantry Tank Mk
IV, Churchill II, with a
2pdr gun was an early
mark of Churchill, shown
in service in 1942.
Left Churchill VII Crocodile was a flamethrower
version with a 75 mm gun,
here burning out a pillbox
in October 1944.

The American Heavy Tanks

Classed as a medium tank now, but descended from the heavy tanks of the 1940s, this sandbag-protected M48A3 was pictured in Vietnam.

Like the American light tanks produced in the 1930s and 1940s, the American heavy tank designs of the later years of the Second World War have little claim to fame as examples of original ideas, but the development story does illustrate how the designs of other tanks could exert an influence. For the series which culminated in the very powerful, heavily armed and armoured Pershing (M26) of 1945 was conditioned by the need to produce a big-gun tank able to outfight the German Tiger and Panther tanks in Europe.

Due to differences of opinion between the Ordnance Department and the field army, the introduction of these heavy tanks was delayed until the closing months of the war. In some ways the policy actually adopted – of concentrating on Sherman medium tank production – paid off in that a huge supply of proven tanks was available. Efforts to produce a better medium tank – which ultimately 'grew' into a heavy tank – involved considerable technological effort and great strides were made in only two or three years which changed the shape of the American tank from the simple boxy appearance typified by the Sherman tank to the lower, sleeker, vehicle typified by such models as the M26, M48, and M60.

Once the M4 series had reached production status, consideration was immediately given to its successor. In May 1942 the Ordnance Department received confirmation from the Supply Department that it could go ahead with designing and procuring a pilot model for an improved medium tank, provisionally designated M4X. Broad requirements called for a 32 ton vehicle with automatic 75mm gun, 4in of front armour and a top speed of 25mph. A wooden mock-up was accordingly built by

Fisher Body Co., one of the medium tank producers. By September 1942 it had been agreed after consulting the Armored Forces to build three pilot models of 30 tons maximum weight, each with different armament and interchangeable turrets. The first one, T20, was to have a 76mm gun and HVSS, the second, T20E1, was to have NVSS and a 75mm automatic gun, while the third T20E2, was to have a 3in gun and torsion bar suspension. Each was to be powered by the new Ford GAN V-8 tank engine and have a torque converter and Hydra-matic transmission. The T20 was built by Fisher and completed in June 1943. The T20E1 was cancelled but its turret was used in the later T22E1.

Both the T20 and T20E3 were tested but the transmission system gave much trouble with oil leaks and overheating. Development of these vehicles ceased at the end of 1944, by which time developments had proceeded to much later types. Experience and information gathered from these vehicles under test was useful, however, for development of later T20 range tanks. Maximum armour thickness of these T20 tanks was 62mm at the front, they had a 47 degree sloped hull front, were all welded with a cast turret and featured several standard fittings from the M4 series. In the T20 series drive was to the rear, whereas in the M4 series it was to the front sprockets.

T22 was a further development of the T20 series dating from October 1942. Chrysler were asked to build two pilot tanks identical in all respects to the T20 except for the transmission, which was to be of the same five-speed mechanical type as used in the M4 medium tank. Trouble was experienced with the transmission and rear drive, however, on tests, and work on

160

the T22 project was formally cancelled in December 1944. Both vehicles had been completed in June 1943.

Subsequently the first pilot model was converted to take a special turret with 75mm automatic gun which had been built for the projected T20E1. In its new guise, the T22 was redesignated T22E1. The turret was virtually a lengthened M4 type, the gun was the standard M3 weapon, and the mount was the standard M34 type. Main feature was the automatic hydraulic loader with two magazines, one for HE and one for AP ammunition, selected remotely as required by the commander who was located in the left rear of the turret. The only other turret occupant was the gunner, and there was no loader. Tests gave a maximum rate of fire of 20 rounds per minute, but the magazines and loading mechanism were unreliable. Production of such a turret, to very compact dimensions, was a considerable technical achievement, but by this time there was a requirement for a heavier calibre gun, and the project was cancelled in December 1944.

Development of another design of the T23 was authorized at the same time as that of the T22. Hull, armament, and general layout were similar to the T22, but vertical volute suspension and tracks as used on the M4 series were to be used and electric transmission was specified. As with the T22, three pilot models were asked for, the T23 with 76mm gun, the T23E1 with 75mm automatic gun, and the T23E2 with 3in gun. However, as in the T20 series, the projects for vehicles with 75mm gun and 3in gun were cancelled before completion. The T23 pilot model was, in fact, the first of the T20 type tanks to be completed, finished by Detroit Arsenal in January 1943 and under test before either the T20 or T22. A second pilot model was ready by March 1943. The pilot models were tested at Fort Knox and proved to be very manoeuvrable. In May 1943 a 'limited procurement' order of 250 vehicles was commended, subjected to detail improvements in the design. These tanks were built by Detroit Arsenal between November 1943 and December 1944, differing from the pilot models in having an all-round vision cupola for the commander, a rotating hatch for the loader, an improved gun mount (the T80), and an improved 76mm gun, the M1A1. Though used in limited numbers in America, the T23 was never standardized and never generally issued or used in combat.

The main reason for this was that Army Ground Forces were already quite satisfied with the M4 medium tank while the Armored Force Board considered some T23 features unsatisfactory, in particular poor weight distribution, excessive ground pressure, and the mode of

Top to bottom Medium Tanks T20, T22, and T23, all developed as possible M4 Sherman replacements. Only the T23 saw production in limited numbers.

electric transmission which was untried in the long term and possibly suspect. They requested ten T23s for further trials in an attempt to overcome these shortcomings. First of these ordered was designated T23E3 and was to have torsion bar suspension and 19in tracks, while the second, T23E4 was to have horizontal volute suspension (an improvement over vertical volute suspension) and wide tracks. This latter vehicle was subsequently cancelled however.

The T23E3, completed by Chrysler at Detroit Arsenal in August 1944, had a turret taken from a production T23 and torsion bar suspension taken from the T25E1. All other features were the same as the T23 but the turret basket was eliminated to give increased ammunition stowage and the electric transmission was fully waterproofed, a retrospective modification also featured in late production T23s. On the basis of experience with the T20E3, which had by this time been completed with torsion bar suspension, the Ordnance Department requested in

A tank recovery vehicle
M32B3 in service with the
Israeli Defence Forces
tows a disabled Super
Sherman out of the firing
line. This is the American-
developed recovery
version of the Sherman
tank and is winch- and
jib-fitted with a fixed
superstructure in place of
the turret on the gun tank.

Top Medium Tank T25.
Above Medium Tank
T25E1; these photographs show how the
eventual M26 shape
evolved.

these being the first vehicles completed in the T20–T23 range. In April 1943, Army Service Forces gave approval for the procurement of 50 trial vehicles, based on the T23 but mounting 90mm guns. Of these, 40 were to have the same basic armour characteristics as the T23 and would be designated T25, while the other 10 were to have increased armour protection to provide a 'heavy' medium tank of comparable performance and immunity to the German Tiger tank which had just then made its appearance in action in Tunisia. The heavier design was to be designated T26.

Detroit Arsenal built two pilot models of the T25, completing them in January and April 1944 respectively. These had HVSS and 23 in wide tracks, and Ford engine and electric transmission as in the T23. The hull was reinforced with a ribbed hull top to support the massive cast turret and had internal modifications to allow the stowage of 90mm ammunition. By the time the T25 pilot models were tested at Fort Knox interest had switched to the T25E1 design, which came about when design studies for the T25 showed that this vehicle with its electric transmission would weigh rather more than 40 tons.

To reduce weight as much as possible it was decided to drop the electric transmission and revert to the Hydra-matic type transmission with torque converter as had been fitted in the T20 medium tank. Accordingly the order for 40 T25s was switched to this modified design and designated T25E1. Grand Blanc Arsenal (Fisher), the contractors, completed the first in January 1944 and finished the production run the following May. By this time, however, with the invasion of Europe approaching, attention had switched to the more heavily armoured T26 series and the 40 T25E1 vehicles were used solely for tests and development work. The T25E1 differed from the T25 in having torsion bar suspension and a modified hull as well as different transmission.

Simultaneously with the design of the T25, further designs were drawn up for a more heavily armoured version of the same tank, designated T26. This would have had electric transmission, as in the T25. Development studies showed that both the T25 and T26 with this transmission would again be excessively heavy, the T26 weighing more than 45 tons. In view of this, the T25 was redesigned with Torque-matic transmission (Hydra-matic transmission with a torque converter) and the same changes were, of course, incorporated in the T26 design. Only the T26 pilot model was therefore built and the 10 scheduled production vehicles for test purposes were all completed as T26E1s. The T26E1 was similar in most char-

July 1943 that the T23E3 be standardized as the Medium Tank M27 and the T20E3 be standardized as the M27B1 both for immediate production in view of the fact that the M4 medium tanks would be seriously obsolescent by 1944. This was rejected by the Army, however, and no further progress was made with standardizing the T23 series.

In the event, however, this led to numerous improvements being made in the M4 series for introduction from late 1943 onwards and many of the features tried or developed in the T20–T23 tanks were incorporated into M4 Sherman vehicles, in particular the complete T23 type turret and 76mm gun, the horizontal volute spring suspension, and the simplified 47 degree hull front. Thus, while the T20–T23 series vehicles did not see general service or combat, they played a most important part in US tank development in the late war period, leading to improvements in the M4 design and, as developed into the T25 and T26, to the evolution of the M26 heavy tank.

An important step in the evolution of the American heavy tank came next. In September 1942 when the T20 design was drawn up, the Ordnance Department suggested that a 90mm gun be developed for mounting in future tanks of this series. By March 1943, such a weapon had been produced in prototype form and mounted for tests in one of the T23 pilot models,

acteristics to the T25E1 but had wider tracks (24in), increased overall width, a shorter hull, increased armour maximum (100mm), and a correspondingly increased weight.

In September 1943, the Ordnance Department urged immediate production of 500 T25E1s and 500 T26E1s for delivery in 1944, but this was opposed by both the Armored Force Board, who would have preferred the 90mm gun mounted in the M4 medium tank, and by the commander of Army Ground Forces, who did not consider a 90mm gun desirable in a tank since it would encourage tank units to stalk enemy tanks, a role assigned to tank destroyers in the then-current armour doctrine of the US Army. The Army instead requested in April 7000 T25E1s with 75mm guns and 1000 T26E1s armed with a 76mm gun. This clearly impractical request – which would have involved further development work and, in any case, duplicated existing types with smaller calibre guns – was not resolved until June 1944 when all the T26E1 development vehicles had been completed. On June 1, a statement came from the European Theatre of Operations that they required no new vehicles with 75mm or 76mm guns in 1945; instead they wanted tanks with 90mm and 105mm weapons in the ratio 1:4. Their request was upheld by the Army Staff and the T26E1 underwent its trials programme as planned. At the end of June 1944 the T26E1 was reclassified Heavy Tank T26E1 and became the prototype for the M26 Pershing.

Extensive trials were carried out with the ten T26E1 pilot models by the Ordnance Department and numerous detail modifications were made for incorporation in production vehicles. These included improvements to the transmission and the engine cooling, revisions in the electrical system, removal of the turret cage to increase ammunition stowage, improved engine access, and larger air cleaners.

In August 1944, the Ordnance Department recommended that the T26E1 should be standardized and placed into production. Opposition from the user arms was still strong, however, and the Army stated that the vehicle could not be standardized until the Armored Force Board had also tested and approved the production modifications. Earlier, in July, the Army Command had tried another delaying move by requesting that the T26E1 be redesigned with the 76mm gun, a retrograde proposal ignored by the Ordnance Department. It was not until December 1944 that the T26E1 was approved for 'limited procurement' and production vehicles, with the various modifications earlier suggested, were designated T26E3 to distinguish them from the pilot models.

Production of the first 20 T26E3s had begun

One of the first M26 Heavy Tanks at Neufelden, Austria, in early May 1945, just before the ending of war.

in November and the Ordnance Department proposed early in December that these be shipped straight to Europe for combat testing. Once again the Army was opposed to the idea and asked that they first go to the Armored Force for testing and 'certification of battleworthiness'. This would have wasted yet another month. However, within a week of this exchange, two German panzer armies savagely hammered the US 1st Army in the lightning Ardennes Offensive of December 1944. Among other things, this reverse spotlighted the inadequacies of the M4 medium with its relatively light armour and 76mm gun; undoubtedly this was a factor which caused the American General Staff to intervene in the T26 affair on December 22, and order immediate shipment of available T26E3s to Europe without further testing.

The first 20 T26E3s were shipped to Europe in January 1945 and at the beginning of February they were issued for service to the 3rd and 9th Armored Divisions. The near successful Ardennes Offensive (Battle of the Bulge) vindicated the Ordnance Department's persistent attempts to get a tank with a 90mm gun into service. In January 1945 the Army had no hesitation in agreeing that the T26E3 should be considered battleworthy, and the cry for more vehicles came from Europe where tank crews were favourably impressed with the new tank which was nearly a match for the Tiger in a straight shooting match, and very much more mobile. Full production of the T26E3 was ordered in January 1945 and it was built by Grand Blanc Arsenal (1190) and later Detroit Arsenal (246). In March 1945 the T26E3 was standardized as the Heavy Tank M26 and it was named 'General Pershing', usually short-

Right M37 tank of the Lebanon Army on border patrol near Rachaya in the late 1960s. *Below* Backbone of the US Army's armoured forces in the late 1960s was the medium tank M48A2, with 90mm gun. These vehicles are at Tay Minh, Vietnam, in 1970.

Post-war developments from the M26 Heavy Tanks. *Above left* M46. *Above right* M47 in Bundeswehr service, 1968. *Right* M47 of the Jordanian Royal Armoured Corps, March 1960. *Below* Combat Tank 90mm M48A2.

ened to 'Pershing'. Later in 1945, the M26 saw action in the Pacific, being used in the taking of Okinawa.

The 90mm M3 gun still had slightly inferior hitting power to the German Tiger with its 88mm gun. To improve the performance of the M26 a new longer gun was developed, the T54, which fired fixed ammunition using a larger cartridge case. This weapon had a concentric recoil mechanism. Two pilot models (designated M26E1) with the new gun were approved in May 1945, but no production order followed due to the cessation of hostilities.

The M26 Pershing was thus a far cry from the M4 Sherman, though its development had been initiated as simply an improved Sherman. Some Pershings were delivered to Britain in 1946 and others later went to other American allies. After its very short development time, the M26 set the pattern followed for the next 30 years or so by the American armour designs. The M46, M47, M48, and M60, all followed essentially the same layout as the Pershing, though there were many improvements – new engines, new turrets, new guns, new control systems, and modified suspension, were the major changes over the years.

A 'Heavy Combat Team' of special variants on the M26 chassis was proposed. These included the M45, with 105mm howitzer replacing the gun, T48 8in howitzer motor carriage, and T92/T93 motor carriages. Prototypes of these huge and imposing vehicles were built but they saw little or no service due to the ending of the war.

The 'Heavy Weight Combat Team' vehicles had some interesting features. For example, the T26E5 was a heavy assault version of the M26 with thicker frontal armour on hull, turret, and mantlet. In its final form it had a heavier turret with 11in of armour on the mantlet and 6in of frontal armour on the hull. Weight was 51 tons. The track was permanently fitted with grousers. Classified 'limited procurement', 27 were built, commencing in June 1945, all at Detroit Arsenal. The added weight of the T26E5 had an adverse effect on performance and this vehicle was not considered entirely satisfactory.

To meet the requirement from Europe for tanks with the 105mm howitzer, a weapon of this calibre was tested in a T23 medium tank. In June 1944 this was dropped in favour of the same weapon in the T26E1. Designated T26E2, the vehicle had a redesigned turret to take the howitzer, and modified ammunition stowage. A heavier turret front was fitted to maintain equilibrium of the turret with the lighter weapon. In July 1945 the T26E2 was classified a 'limited procurement' type and redesignated M45. Only a few were produced.

The M26 Pershing set the pattern for the American main battle tanks through to the 1970s and beyond. Improvements were swiftly made to the basic M26 design, however. In 1946 a technical committee reviewed mechanical progress with wartime designs and commended the adoption of a new standard tank engine with 'cross drive' transmission derived from the Hydra-matic and Torque-matic drives used on later wartime tanks. As an interim measure the M26 was refitted with the new engine and transmission and was redesignated M46 in this form.

Meantime an entirely new medium tank was being designed, the T42. This was based closely on the M26 but was fabricated from flat plates to simplify production. Its turret included a built-in rangefinder. However, this vehicle never entered production for by this time, 1950, the Korean War had started and there was an urgent need for tanks in quantity. The T42 turret, already in production ahead of the T42, was fitted to the M46 and the new vehicle, recognized from the start as an interim type, was designated M47. The early vehicles were, in fact, modified M46s, but later new vehicles were built to the design. Because of the slightly increased length consequent upon fitting of the new engine and drive, a distinctive small 'jockey' wheel was fitted into the suspension ahead of the sprocket.

The M47 was very widely used, being supplied to almost every nation within the American sphere of influence, including West Germany, Japan, Nationalist China, Belgium, France, Jordan, and Jugoslavia. Its very availability made it an important part of the West's armoury in the 'Cold War' years, despite several shortcomings (in particular it was a rather complicated vehicle which required a high degree of crew training).

Concurrent with the M47 procurement, work was put in hand on a new design to replace it, the T48, which was finally contracted for with Ford Motor Co. and Fisher Body in March 1951. Because the Korean War was at its height the design was pushed through at a great rate and this caused an enormous number of technical problems which dogged the vehicle's fortunes for years. Range was limited, construction and maintenance were complicated. It was not until the 1960s, with the M48A2, that most of the problems were overcome. In 1960 came a much improved vehicle, the M60, which was in essence the M48 with the British designed 105mm L351 gun. In the 1970s the M60A1 with several variants, including the M60A1E1 with Shillelegh missile, formed the main backbone of US armoured forces, a direct descendant of the M26 of 1944.

America's main battle tank of the 1970s, the M60A1, developed through the M26/M46/M47/M48 line, also serves with several nations traditionally supplied by the USA. These are Israeli vehicles at Suez in October 1973. The M60A1 has the same British-developed 105 mm gun as the Centurion.

The Russian Heavy Tanks

The squat low shape of the JS-3 and its 122mm gun made it the best armoured and armed tank in the world in the 1940s.

The 'inverted fry pan' turret, faceted glacis, and infra-red night fighting searchlight are all well shown from this angle.

Last word in this study of the great tanks must go to the Russians, whose mastery at building a fine medium tank, the T-34, was matched by their ability to build a series of effective and dominating heavy tanks, culminating in the Josef Stalin series, which in turn influenced the designs of the main battle tanks of the West in the post-war years.

In the 1930s the Russians followed the trend set by the British 'Independent' tank and, like the French and Germans, put into service large multi-turreted tanks – sometimes known jocularly as 'robber baron's castles' – which could operate virtually isolated as a mobile fortress. The T-32 and T-35 were produced resembling the 'Independent' and with a 76mm gun in the main turret and various smaller guns in four auxiliary turrets. A smaller vehicle, rated as a medium tank, was the T-28 which was of similar configuration.

By 1938 a new generation of heavy tanks was being planned at the Leningrad tank factory, with I.S. Kotin heading the design team. They schemed out what amounted to direct replacements for the T-35, the T-100 and SMK, both similar in appearance but differing in detail. Two turrets were fitted, each on the centre line. The forward turret had a 45mm gun, the larger a 76mm gun, and this was arranged in a barbette,

super-firing as in a warship. The actual hull structure almost duplicated that of the T-35, but the old box bogies and side skirts were dropped in favour of simple torsion bar suspension which was virtually a copy of that fitted in the then new PzKpfw III.

These new tanks were very heavy (weighing about 56 tons) and needed big crews of six or more men. The cast armour was up to 60mm thick, making the tank virtually immune to fire from contemporary 37mm anti-tank guns.

Legend credits Stalin himself with the suggestion for a lightened version of the SMK/T-100 with one turret eliminated (like Hitler, Stalin took a personal interest in tanks). More probably, Kotin drew up designs for both twin turret models and a single turret model, and Stalin expressed a preference for the latter. At all events after the SMK/T-100 prototypes were completed, Kotin turned his attention to detailed design of a single turret version and the prototype vehicle was completed in September 1939. This was quickly followed by a few pre-production vehicles which saw action against the Finns in the Russo–Finnish war of December 1939. The SMK/T-100 prototypes were also exposed to action on the Finnish front and proved to be too big and slow for comfort, falling victims to determined Finnish attacks.

Right The T-28, seen here in 1940 exercises, was typical of the large tanks of the 1930s, though this one was classed as a 'medium'. An even larger similar design was the T-35.
Far right The KV-1, in service in 1940, replaced the earlier models.

The single turret version was meanwhile put into production and named Klimenti Voroshilov after the famous Soviet general – KV for short. There were a number of KV production models and the detail variations between them were quite considerable, although superficially all had common characteristics. The design was extremely functional and uncluttered. A simple box-like body with a cast nose had an armour maximum of 75mm. The 76·2mm gun was the same model as mounted in the T-34. The same V-2 diesel motor of the T-34 powered the KV and many fittings were common. Maximum standardization of components and layout was one of the lessons the Soviets learned very early and this contributed in no small way to Russian success in the field of armour in the Second World War. In a way standardization was an enforced necessity to make the best use of the country's limited industrial and technological resources.

The KV-1 was complemented by the KV-II which was actually a mobile artillery piece rather than a tank. In place of the standard turret, a massive box-like turret with a 152mm howitzer was fitted. It was not very successful, its height providing a generous target; as a bombardment vehicle against the Mannerheim line the KV-II had a brief moment of glory in 1940. In 1941, however, it proved no match for German 'blitzkrieg' tactics, and production ceased. The KV-1 continued to be developed over the next two years or so. The 1941 production model was up-armoured by the addition of extra armour plate on nose, hull front, and turret to combat the larger calibre German anti-tank guns then entering service. Even then the vehicle could not be made entirely immune to anti-tank gun fire, and a 1942–43 model was the KV-1s (s: skorostnoi: fast). Here the armour was reduced and the transmission improved, resulting in a weight decrease from 47 to 42 tons and a speed increase from 22 to 25mph.

By mid-1943 the German Tiger was in service and the need for more powerful guns in tanks was urgent. This led to the KV-85, which had a slightly widened hull to accommodate a cast turret and an 85mm gun very similar to that fitted in the T-34/85.

The KV-85 exhausted the potential as a gun tank. For a larger gun a larger turret ring was needed, and in 1943 the design team looked at the KV again and solved the problem quite simply. It seems very probable that they were inspired by the German Tiger tank which was then being encountered. The top run of the tracks was lowered, along with the return rollers, sprocket and idlers, and the hull top was extended sideways to form panniers over the

tracks, and faired into the nose. This gave the necessary width for a larger turret ring. After a brief trial with a 100mm gun it was found possible to carry a massive 122mm gun adapted from a corps artillery gun, thus providing the vehicle with an advantage of firepower of considerable magnitude, still not surpassed 30 years later.

The new vehicle was, inevitably enough, named Josef Stalin, and this was the most powerfully armed tank of the war. Mechanically similar to the KV, the JS-1 incorporated the sloped back hull of the T-34 and a heavy cast turret. Problems with the 122mm gun included a big reduction in space for ammunition stowage, a slower rate of fire, and cramped crew conditions, but these factors were outweighed by the sheer firepower of the piece. No other tank could outshoot it (although by 1945 the Germans did develop the huge Jagdtiger with 128mm gun).

In 1944 Kotin improved on the original design with the JS-2, over 2000 of which were built. The nose was reshaped and the sides

Newly delivered KV-Is on exercises in wooded country in late 1941. Note the horn periscopes on the turret top, simple vision slits and vision blocks, and the rough weld seams.

The immensely high KV-2 had a short 152mm howitzer and was, strictly speaking, a self-propelled gun rather than a tank. The vehicle was somewhat vulnerable, being both high and slow due to the great weight of the turret and gun. Vehicles with limited traverse mounts were developed to replace it.

In a direct line of development from the T-34, the T-62, produced in the 1960s, is built with characteristic Russian ruggedness and functionism. Its 120mm gun fires fin-stabilised rounds, being smooth bore to give high velocity. *Right* A T-62 of the Syrian Army knocked out in the 1973 war. *Below* A captured T-62 in service with the Israeli Defence Force in 1974.

SU-152, first on KV, then on JS running gear, replaced the KV-2. *Below* JS-2 (and earlier JS-1) were developed in 1943–44 from the KV. *Bottom* The JS-3 made its first public appearance in the Victory Parade in Berlin in 1945, and overnight rendered most other tanks obsolescent.

tidied up, resulting in a slightly lighter vehicle. But better was to come, and in late 1944 Kotin completely redesigned the hull and turret shape to produce what became the most sensational tank to emerge from the Second World War, the classic JS-3. This first appeared early in 1945 but too late to see action. Its first real appearance was at the Allied Victory parade in Berlin 1945 when the JS-3 presented a major surprise to the observers from the West. Overnight it rendered almost all other tank designs virtually obsolete.

The JS-3 revolutionized the shape of the tank. Its superstructure sloped all round and the multi-faceted nose was angled and faired into the hull sides. The turret was of the 'inverted frying pan' type, ballistically superb, eliminating all shot traps, and keeping the silhouette low – only a fraction over 8ft. In almost all the main battle tanks designed in the West after 1945 these features were copied, so that such types as the West German Leopard, the French AMX 30, and the British Chieftain all perpetuate the low sleek shape originated by the JS-3. The later Russian medium tanks, the T-54 and T-62, also adopted the characteristic 'turtle' or 'frying pan' turret shape and the low height.

The KV/JS chassis also formed the basis for a big family of heavy self-propelled guns – the JSU-122 and JSU-151 were the most notable – which appeared in 1943–44. After the war the chassis was also used as a carrier for tactical battlefield missiles, and there was also a recovery vehicle version. A 1950 development was the T-10, simply an enlarged lengthened version of the JS-3, with all the same characteristics but featuring infra-red night sights and other technical improvements.

Armament in the West was geared to combating the JS-3 and its massive gun. In the 1950s both the British (with the Conqueror) and the Americans (M103) put into service huge and expensive heavy tanks solely designed to outshoot the JS-3 on the battlefield. But like the wartime German heavy tanks these big vehicles were tactically limited in use and they had short lives. The JS-3 itself was outmoded by the early 1960s for the Soviets had developed late model T-54 and T-62 medium tanks which could undertake the main battle tank role. By the 1970s even the role and value of the main battle tank was being questioned, following the widespread introduction of wire-guided anti-tank missiles and other specialist small anti-tank missiles. The Israeli–Arab war of late 1973 vividly demonstrated that the conventional main battle tank – as the medium tank of old had become – was now itself highly vulnerable to the missile and by the mid-1970s there was every indication that the small light tank, itself missile armed, indicated the trend for the future.